Unaccustomed As I Am

Unaccustomed as I Am

Brian Quinn

Twenty-six tales of fiction, parody and personal mishap

Penny Post

Published in 2020 by Penny Post Limited, www.pennypost.org.uk

© Brian Quinn 2020

A CIP record for this book is available from the British Library.

Printed in the UK by 4Edge Limited

ISBN: 978-1-8382580-0-9

For Penny, Michael, Dominic, Adam and Toby

*Many thanks to all those who gave me encouragement and
practical support in preparing this book, with particular thanks to
Oliver Keen, Christopher Turner, Dr Jennifer Davis, Cathy and Steve Edis,
Alex and Emma Milne-White, Jon Crowcroft, Nick Lumley and David Seaton:
and – above all – to Penny, without whom...*

Contents

Unaccustomed as I Am

LEAFING THROUGH THE newspaper the other day, my eye was caught by an article about Kit & McConnel's caberet act. The name 'Kit' and the mention of 'cabaret' stirred a memory. Could this be the same Kit who, then in a partnership called Kit and the Widow, locked me out of the dining hall at Queens' College Cambridge where I was compèring an event at a May Ball all those years ago, forcing me to climb through a lavatory window and leading to a state of confusion that made me insult Noël Coward's pianist? A few minutes' research on the internet showed that it was.

This event happened in June 1980 at the end of my last term at Queens' during May Week (in fact ten days or so in June) at which time May Balls were, and probably still are, held by most of the colleges. The organising committees were composed of students, smart cookies when dealing with the works of Plato or the melting point of potassium but ill-prepared when it came to the rapacious demands of marquee hire firms, champagne merchants and musical agents. The result was that ticket prices increased to stratospheric levels. No one seemed to mind: there were enough people who were prepared to pay what was charged and plenty of others for whom the high prices gave an added incentive to break into the events, which was quite easy. Any shortfall was deftly apportioned elsewhere by the college bursar. This combination of improvidence and financial chicanery was in some ways a foretaste of the banking crisis of 2008. Indeed, this catastrophe was probably caused by exactly the same people, now no longer ratty students but sleek plutocrats, more at ease with handling vast sums of money but no less careless about the consequences of their profligacy.

If you worked at the May Ball you obviously didn't have to pay to get in. Somehow I wangled or was persuaded to undertake – I can't now remember which – the position of compère at the 'cabaret' which took place in the medieval dining hall, a place of elaborate cornices, minstrel galleries and eternal draughts. All I had to do was to ensure that the stage was set for each act and then introduce them. What could possibly go wrong?

The day came and there I was, already fortified by several glasses of something or other. In the afternoon I met the various performers, most of whom didn't seem to know or greatly care what they wanted for their staging or even what exactly they were going to be doing in their performance. The atmosphere was one of light-hearted and slightly intoxicated amateurism, into which my personality fits so easily. All this changed with the arrival of Kit and the Widow and Tarrington Bradwell.

I may have got the last name wrong but it certainly presented numerous possibilities for inadvertent Spoonerisms. He was a thin, elderly, waspish man, exactly the sort of person who would have played piano for Noël Coward. He was very precise. The piano, he told me, was to be just *here*, at this angle; this table was to be *there*; the vase of flowers was to be *here*, like *that*. I barely listened to what appeared to be absurd requests; but already there was the sense in the back of my mind that I'd miscounted the trumps in this gig.

Kit and the Widow were clearly a dangerous pair, I could tell that at once. For one thing, like Mr Bradwell, they knew exactly what they were about; there was also a wicked gleam in their eyes that hinted at trouble brewing for those who crossed them. Their various requests were elaborate and in some cases – as I think they knew – impossible to fulfil. Where, at this stage, was I going to get a large stuffed animal from? The Master's Lodge? I was now getting alarmed. A free ticket, and for an event I was not going to be able to enjoy, suddenly seemed not nearly enough payment.

The clock ticked round to ten o'clock and the cabaret began. After dealing successfully with the first few acts I began to relax slightly. The audience was benign and the performers seemed mainly to be trying out new material and had no expectations of a rousing reaction. Over-confidence, and a bit more wine, kicked in. Then Kit and the Widow's first turn of the evening started. Everything went downhill pretty fast after that.

I think it all started because the piano was in completely the wrong place and some of the props were missing. Even I realised that I was screwing up. After their first act there was to be a short interval which I spent trying to inject some professionalism into what I was doing. I was certainly flustered and may well have become fussy. What I was unprepared for was, just before the end of the interval, being firmly pushed out through a doorway by Kit and being told 'you'll have to go, you're just being far too camp.' Given the double entendre-laden nature of their act, I found this an astonishing judgement. I was still thinking about this when I heard a key turn in the lock.

I was in a small side room at the back of the hall. There were three doors and no windows. Two of the doors were locked, one before the show had started, the other just now by Kit. The third led to some toilets; here there was a small window which opened onto one of the quads. There seemed nothing else for it.

On all the occasions when I've had to climb in or out of a toilet window I've ended up breaking something, tearing something or falling into the urinal. All three things happened this time. My right shoe slipped and got soaked almost immediately. The window catch caught on and ripped my shirt, then broke off. I just managed to squeeze through and ended up in a bush, my shin colliding with a hard object that turned out to be the base of an ornamental urn that had probably been sitting there since the Wars of the Roses. I emerged having briefly lost all sense of direction and set off towards the wrong building. When I finally returned to the hall, panting, dishevelled and bleeding slightly, I found that the first act had already started. Of all the humiliations recently visited upon me this was perhaps the worst. It proved that my presence was unnecessary, even a hindrance, and that my whole involvement in the event was a colossal waste of time.

Thus chastened, I returned backstage where Kit and the Widow were lurking. If they noticed my torn shirt, muddy shoes, loosened tie and the odour of urine and sweat they gave no sign of it. I said nothing to them. There seemed to be nothing to say.

I mechanically went through the rest of the introductions but felt more and more as if I were somewhere else. I even managed to introduce Kit and the Widow's second act without screwing up my lines or getting re-ejected from the hall. I was almost starting to relax again. Then, whether because of over-confidence or drink or something else, it all, right at the end, went very badly wrong again.

I suppose the fact that the earlier distractions had driven all of Tarrington Bradwell's instructions from my mind didn't help: nor did the fact that I'd decided to dispense with my shoes and had taken off my tie. When Mr B saw how all his requests had been ignored he started making venomous hissing noises. These turned out to be instructions to put this here, and that there, and look sharp about it. I don't know what the audience thought was going on: a piece of experimental mime, perhaps. Finally the stage was set to his liking. He gestured that he was ready to be announced. I turned to the audience and raised by hands. The hall fell silent. To my horror, I felt my mind go completely blank.

What *was* the man's name? I had about five seconds before I had to say something. This proved to be not nearly long enough. 'Ladies and gentlemen,' I began. No name suggested itself. My dealings with him during the set-up seemed to be from another age. It was by now probably about 3am. Why couldn't the bloody man have a proper, normal name? Mind you, at that moment even 'John Smith' would have been beyond me.

Something had to give. I recalled a couple of the syllables and decided to mash them together into something that at least sounded right. By that point nothing was making much sense. My overriding desire was to get off the stage and get all these people to look at someone other than me. I had nothing to offer them.

'Jadies and lentlemen,' I said at last, 'Mr Barrington Treadwell.' I turned and stumbled away. As I did so, I caught Tarrington Bradwell's eye. I don't think I've ever seen anyone so unpleasantly affected by a sentence containing only six words. As I collapsed backstage, Kit and the Widow were there, grinning at me. For them, the whole evening had doubtless been a great success, despite or perhaps partly because of my 'camp' performance.

I remember nothing about the rest of the evening.

If there's one thing this event taught me it was that I should never, ever appear on a stage again nor try to speak unprepared in public, resolutions which I have very nearly kept. For Kit and the Widow, it was the start of a glorious career. As for Tarrington Bradwell, for all I know he quietly changed his name to Barrington Treadwell, gave up the stage altogether and spent the rest of his life growing roses in Pinner.

So, Kit, if you need a compère for your next tour, don't give me a ring. Whenever it is, I'll be doing my hair, painting my nails and generally camping it up like nobody's business. But break a leg, my dear. God knows, you almost caused me to break one of mine.

Five a Day

I'VE BEEN LUCKY. Only twice have I seen large amounts of blood. Both times it was mine, both times from being hit on the right side of my nose. The first time I had a door kicked open in my face. The second time I was beaten up by a greengrocer.

The first is as it sounds: could happen to anyone. The second is more complicated.

It was a bitingly cold day in North London in that bitingly cold winter of 1982. Everyone's nerves were on edge and nobody's more so than the guy on the fruit and veg stall in Caledonian Road. He wasn't the usual bloke with whom I would chat about football when he was weighing my potatoes but a tough-looking character with a twitchy expression that, had I been older and wiser, I would have known spelled trouble.

My turn came. I asked for eight oranges. The sign, apostrophe and all, said '8 orange's – 80p'. He charged me £1.60. I complained. He said 'you what?' I said 'it's 80p.' Then his fist slammed into my nose. I fell over. Sprawled would be a better word.

Some years later, the boxer Mike Tyson made his famous remark that 'everyone has a plan until they're hit in the face.' He was right. After a moment you recover but the world is a darker and more confusing place. Without any clear idea of what was going to happen next, I started to stand up.

The trader wasn't having any of that and kicked me hard in the shoulder. I fell over again.

I wish I could remember the reaction of the people around me. This was a violent time but not a particularly violent neighbourhood. I certainly got no support.

Again I tried to stand up and again he hit me. This was no brief red mist: I was dealing with a border-line psycho probably intent on finishing me off. Even so, I couldn't spend the rest of the day on the pavement. I raised myself onto all fours and slowly got to my feet while backing away from him. It was an awful shambling, abject performance, like a slave abasing himself in front of Nero.

His mate stepped forward and gave me a kick. "Why don't you piss off?" he suggested. "Do you want to stay a git all your life?"

It didn't seem worth arguing about. Finally I was allowed to get to my feet. Once upright, I felt that I ought to do or say something. Fortunately I decided not to.

"If I was you," a woman said, "don't change your clothes before you go to the doctor." I looked down. I was covered in blood. "That way they'll see you quicker. Shocking, the time you have to wait." She handed me a tissue. Behind her, the trader and his mate carried on as if nothing had happened.

I followed her advice. The surgery was about half a mile away. The waiting room seemed, after the freezing street, incredibly hot. I eventually saw a young doctor who was so tired she could hardly keep her eyes open.

"You've broken your nose." I knew this already. "Tetanus?"

"What?" It sounded as if she was offering me a drink.

"When did you last have a tetanus shot?"

"I don't know."

She rolled her eyes, or what little I could see of them, produced a hypodermic and squirted something into my arm. Then she gave me some tablets. "The blue ones help the swelling. The white ones help the pain. One each five times a day." She said something about alcohol but I missed that. "Tomorrow, make an appointment at the Whittington for exactly a week's time. Call this number." She gave me a card. There was a pause.

"Good-bye," I said. She didn't reply.

I asked the receptionist for a glass of water and knocked back two of each of the tablets. I walked home, carefully avoiding the market.

For the first time since the attack I examined myself in a mirror. It could have been a lot worse. My nose was about double its normal size across the bridge and my right eye was closing up. I looked as if I'd been beaten up, which was fair enough. I had a shower and a can of beer and felt a whole lot better.

What I ought to have done was go to bed. Then I remembered I'd arranged to meet a friend to see a retro film at seven o'clock. I checked my watch. Just gone six. Perfect timing.

I arrived and told Jon the story. We necked a couple of beers and then it was show time. The usherette handed me some glasses.

"What are these for?"

"It's in 3D."

I'd forgotten this. There had been a brief vogue for 3D films in the 1950s. To exploit the technology there were plenty of fights, bird attacks and other sudden and dramatic movements towards the viewer. Plot, dialogue and acting were secondary.

The first problem was that, with my nose the shape it was, the glasses wouldn't fit. I had a choice: hold them over my eyes, which made my nose throb; or let them sit where they would and see the film out of register with angry flecks of red and green around every object. I chose the second. The movie made no sense but every three minutes or so something was thrown, or flew, or was fired towards the camera. Each time the audience squealed. Once the woman next to me let out a scream so loud I nearly lost my reason. About this time I realised that the effects of the various drugs and the beer were kicking in and combining in unexpected ways. The cinema was very hot. I started to sweat profusely.

It was just after I had had a cat and a saucepan thrown at me that I experienced what I term my First Psychotic Episode. This took the form of a slow-motion re-enactment of the assault superimposed on the meaningless action of the film. I briefly felt I was dying. Maybe I was. I might have screamed but if so it's unlikely anyone noticed. This all lasted about ten seconds: then reality, or what passed for it in that cinema, settled on me again and I was OK.

I was glad when the film finished.

What I should then have done was go home. Instead we had a couple of drinks, during the second of which I knocked back six pills, and decided to go half way across town to see some friends.

An hour later I was sitting in an armchair in Golders Green with a glass of wine, watching *The Big Sleep* and surrounded by people arguing about who killed the chauffeur.

Raymond Chandler wrote superb dialogue and had an uncanny eye for description, for mood and – often underestimated, this one – for nature. As most of his time was, because of his fondness for whisky, spent in much the same condition I was in then, his plots tended to suffer. No one knows who killed the chauffeur in *The Big Sleep*: not even, as was revealed when the film's screenwriters called him up to check this point, Chandler himself. That didn't stop Julian and Simon arguing about it, endlessly.

I felt as if I had a wasp stuck in my head. Just as Marlowe arrived in Realito, my Second Psychotic Episode kicked in. This time the room turned green and red and started to vibrate. The argument seemed to be in a foreign language. My hands went numb. There was a bitter taste in my mouth. I got up, collapsed on the floor behind the armchair and slept for fourteen hours. When I woke up my nose hurt like hell but my brain was well again. I had a cup of tea, threw the rest of the tablets in the bin and went home.

Two days later the usual guy was back on the fruit and veg stand. I told him my story.

"Ah – so *you're* the guy he hit. He's a nutter, isn't he?"

"Well..."

"No, he is. He knocked me out cold last month. He says he's sorry. I think he wants to buy you a pint in the King's Head."

"No thanks."

"Fair enough."

"I never got my oranges."

He poured about twenty into a bag. "There you are." That seemed to be the damages sorted. If this had happened in America a lawyer would have fixed it so I'd never have to work again. Here in England, all I had was the assurance that I wouldn't immediately die of scurvy. I decided to leave it at that.

I kept my appointment at the hospital. I had visions of attractive nurses, gentle sedatives and emerging with a straight nose. All I got was a couple of minutes of disconcerting small talk from a tiny Indian doctor, unexpectedly interrupted by his lunging forward, grabbing my nose and twisting it to the right. I experienced a brief red mist and heard a lot of shouting.

A nurse rushed in. "Are you all right?" she asked. I realised she was talking not to me but to him.

He was very cheerful about it. "People often attack me," he said. "It bloody hurts, I'm told. If you do it a week after the break, much cheaper than operating." He gave me another brilliant smile. "I'm the expert here," he said proudly. "All the busted noses they send straight to me. I save them a bloody fortune."

There were three main results of this fiasco. One, my nose points north-west. Two, I've never liked 3D films. Three, I never argue with greengrocers any more – whatever price they want for their oranges is fine with me. But I still don't know who killed the chauffeur.

Cool in the Pool?

THERE WAS AN article in a recent issue of *Focus*, the popular (in other words, I can understand some of it) science magazine, which argues that it is beneficial for us to be bored from time to time. This experience, so the writer claims, helps us unwind, increases creativity and assists problem solving. I reflected that for once I was reading something commending an aspect of my lifestyle, at least for the two or three hours a week I spend in the pool: for virtually nothing I can think of is as boring as swimming.

Boredom is one of its chief attractions. For maybe three quarters of an hour there's nothing to do apart from count lengths. All other activities are impossible. The digital universe might as well not exist. Starved of input, part of the brain closes down. I find when I emerge that, as well as having shed most of the aches and pains I might have had at the start, my mind has been purged of its various anxieties and confusions. In short, the whole exercise is a restorative one; a form of mobile meditation.

This, at least, is what I tell people. Since reading the *Focus* article I've been giving the matter some thought. Am I quite as pure in the pool as I like to think? I have also reflected on conversations with other regular swimmers and things I have noticed about their behaviour. The reality is a bit less engaging.

I don't suffer from any form of OCD that I'm aware of: not on dry land, anyway. As soon as I see the water and smell the chlorine, this changes. I have a particular locker and cubicle I prefer to use and if either are already occupied I feel a palpable sense of annoyance. I know others feel the same way because I've asked them. I also always start swimming at the shallow end, which is perhaps logical if you don't like diving, but a few people always do it the other way round. Neither of these amount to an obsession but they're slightly worrying deviations from my normal behaviour.

The next issue is the temperature. I swim often enough to be able to tell this to within half a degree from the moment I get in. Humans are not very adaptable, certainly not this one. Anything south of 27° is too cold, north of 32° too hot. Of the two, colder is better and the swim easier. The temperature sets my mood and attitude to the swim. If it's too warm I'll swim more slowly. This may be a self-fulfilling prophecy but I seem incapable of breaking out of it. Again, regular swimmers know the score. "What's the water like?" I once asked Jo, another regular at Hungerford. "Sticky and uphill," she said. I knew exactly what she meant – 31°. It was.

Right, so those hurdles are crossed. I've got changed and got in the water. What's the next problem?

I now have to admit to an even more extreme form of my aquatic OCD: I'm almost incapable of swimming a number of lengths that isn't divisible by eight. This makes some sense as five eights are 40 lengths (a kilometre) and eight eights are 64 lengths (a mile). If I do more than a mile, 72 is a more natural number for me to end on than 70 and 96 more natural than 90. I suppose this is like what some people put up with every day, having to stir a cup of coffee a precise number of times in a particular direction or else it's undrinkable. It's not a welcome habit but one I seem to be stuck with.

During my informal research for this article I told Jim, another regular swimmer, about my obsession with eights and asked if he thought it odd.

"Well, yes," he said.

"Oh." Maybe I was bonkers after all.

"Yes. I always do multiples of ten."

Aside from needing to count in eights or tens as the case may be, the real problem has to do with the very boredom that is also so refreshing. If a thought does get stuck in your head it can become hard to shake. Because swimming is free of normal external stimuli and because you are in a closed world, anything else going on in the pool assumes a vast and immediate significance. As the only other thing going on is other people swimming, it is on them that your attention focusses. Several adults swimming up and down, engaging in a healthy pursuit and shedding their minds and bodies of the aches and anxieties they were suffering from – everyone is relaxed, free of rage and stress, myself included. Or so you might think.

Not a bit of it. We're all different but on dry land these variations are usually ignored. In the water, because we're all doing the same thing, any idiosyncrasies are magnified. Someone swimming in a funny way, or wearing an odd costume, or doing a strange stroke or stopping at odd times – all these things are noticed. Aside from counting, there's nothing else to do but notice, and notice again two lengths later. It's only a short step from regularly noticing something to becoming irritated by it, particularly if in even the smallest way it interacts with what you are doing. (Our own idiosyncrasies we do not, of course, see as annoying to other people at all – it's everyone else who's being weird and difficult, not us.)

As there are never more than three lanes, the most common way we interact with each other is when two or more people in the same lane are swimming at different speeds. There exists an unspoken convention of pausing at the end of a length to let someone behind you pass if they're swimming more quickly than you. A few people just don't get this. When I'm the victim – already my choice of words is becoming adversarial – of this, I'm driven into a condition just slightly short of rage. Only the fact that speech is impossible prevents confrontations. Discreet research amongst other regular swimmers, of both sexes, shows I'm not alone in this reaction.

The other thing about swimming at different speeds is that one sometimes has secret races with other swimmers. A secret race is in a way pathetic, almost child-like: then again, even odder would be to lean across the lane ropes, tap a stranger on the shoulder and say 'last one to the far end and back is a sissy.' No, this is a private game. To someone swimming more slowly, I might say to myself 'I'll do three lengths in the time he takes to do two.' For someone who swims more quickly it might be 'I won't let the bastard catch me up before the end of the next length.' All this passes the time, gets my heart rate up and is fairly harmless. No problems there. However, I'm slightly alarmed by this secretly competitive streak the activity exposes. Ask any other regular swimmer if they do this themselves and most will admit that they do. I don't know many of them that well – indeed many I find hard to recognise when they have their clothes on – but I suspect that most are not this competitive, nor this secretive, on dry land. We thus seem to be dealing with some hitherto unnoticed side-effect of H_2O.

Sometimes these rages or races make me lose track of how many lengths I've swum. I have a rigid rule for coping with that, always going back to the last number I can remember. In most sessions, I therefore swim more lengths than the ones I've counted. If I admit to 80 I might have swum 84, but those extra four didn't officially happen and so don't affect my multiple-of-eight problem. Do you see? It's only the ones that I count that count. If this seems bonkers that's probably because it is. Like any psychopath, I have a cunning and internally consistent logic to explain every aberration.

A certain amount of the time under water is also spent sneering at the peculiar strokes of some people and marvelling at the fluid grace of others. I suspect my own technique doesn't stand up to much scrutiny. My legs tend to twist over when I breathe on the right but not when I breathe on the left. I have no idea why. Clearly my frame is distorted in a way that only this activity reveals. It's not a problem on dry land so I don't then think about it: but in the pool, sometimes for several lengths in a row, I can think about nothing else.

I suppose it's to be expected that our minds play tricks with us during long-ish swims. We are, after all, in an alien environment. We see only a few shades of white and blue. We can taste and smell only chlorine, feel only water, hear only the little waves we make rushing past our ears. We're immersed in a life-giving fluid that will kill us if we breathe it. We're only partly affected by gravity. Most aspects of day-to-day life have been stripped away. It's the closest many of us will get to being in outer space. Is it any wonder that our thought processes can become slightly obsessive? It's as if as soon as we get into the water, and no matter how many times we've done it before, an automatic and ancient part of our brain switches itself on and says, 'listen up – we're in a hazardous situation here. One screw-up and we're toast. I'm in charge. Do what I say or perish!' This isn't a pleasant reaction but perhaps it keeps us alive. It's rather like having a bodyguard permanently standing by your shoulder who, at the first sign of trouble, reaches for his gun and starts barking at you to hit the deck.

At least, that's my story – it's not me that's thinking these things, it's my protector; that or the boredom, playing tricks in my head. Well, no it isn't, not if I'm being honest. I see now I'm abundantly capable of these unworthy and obsessive thoughts all the time but that they are particularly unleashed in this watery world. When I get out of the pool, I am neither so shriven nor so pure as I might like to pretend. In fact, I've passed some of the time peering and poking at the darker parts of my personality and watching them snap and hiss like vipers. If so, maybe it's as well that I've seen a bit more of the man I really am. After a long swim – which is a good thing – I feel almost impossibly self-righteous. These reflections might make me less so. That is a probably a good thing too.

You May Now Turn Over the Paper

THERE WAS A discussion on the radio recently about the value or otherwise of university. One woman put the case against very well: you might make friends and you might deal with great minds but a lot of students don't do much work and miss half their lectures. Even if they learn anything, most of it's completely useless and doesn't teach them any real-life skills.

A harsh judgement, perhaps. However, it well sums up the time I spent studying Medieval History at Cambridge, a combination that provided, I freely admit, a double insulation against the real world which was then dominated by the winter of discontent and the first rumblings of Thatcherism. All problems are relative, of course, and one's own usually more important than anyone else's. My problem, on my third day at Queens', was my first supervision.

The supervision took place in one of the older parts of the college with a man called Jonathan Riley-Smith who was the leading expert, the go-to man as he would be called today, on the subject of the Crusades. I'd met him at my interview for which event he'd made some effort to smarten himself up. For the supervision he made none. Yes, he was wearing a suit but it seemed to have been designed for someone of a different shape. He was constantly shifting his position, giving the impression that at least one item of clothing had been put on back to front. His hair was standing on end – this we both shared – and his tie was creased, stained and poorly knotted. But it was the pipe that cemented the impression of academic central casting. It was either belching evil-smelling smoke, or being held upside down and scattering cinders and ash, or going out altogether. Books and papers were piled up everywhere. The armchairs were of the vague, faded colour that is found nowhere else apart from in dons' studies. The early autumn sunlight shafted through the grimy mullioned windows, illuminating the clouds of smoke that rose whenever Riley-Smith managed to get his pipe going and the clouds of dust whenever he shifted in his seat. The room, the man, the atmosphere – all were exactly what I had expected them to be.

None the less, I was apprehensive. Was he about to ask me some piercing question, laugh at my stumbling reply and then vow never to teach such an imbecile again?

His next remark, though possibly well-meant, was even more disconcerting.

"This," Riley-Smith said, genially waving his pipe around, "is the room in which Erasmus wrote most of his translation of the New Testament."

I glanced around nervously. I was aware that this document had changed the world. Luther and Tyndale had both used it for their vernacular translations in the 1520s which became the sparks that had started the spiritual, intellectual and political fire of the Reformation. It was as if he had confronted me with the piano on which Beethoven had written the Moonlight Sonata, the easel on which Leonardo had propped his canvas before painting the Mona Lisa or the laboratory in which Rutherford had split the atom and said: 'well, that's what's happened so far, now it's your turn – just do your best.'

After this setback we talked for a while about King Edward the Confessor who would, I learned, be the subject of my first essay. After a while I asked him what lectures I should go to.

He grinned and took another formidable pull at his pipe. "That's easy," he said. "None of 'em."

This was unexpected. "But…you're giving some," I replied.

He waved his hand. "Ninth-century France," he said dismissively. "Don't know anything about it. I was drafted in when Baldwin had a heart attack. I wouldn't bother with mine. Most of the others are going to be awful as well."

"Oh. What shall I do?" I sensed I was almost wailing.

He threw out his arms again. "Read, my boy. Read. We have some of the finest libraries in the world here." He gave me a list of a dozen books to get me started and briefly disappeared behind a cloud of smoke. The supervision appeared to be over.

I staggered out and went to the college bar. There I saw Chris, whom I'd met the night before. He was studying Natural Sciences. He said he'd just found out he had hour-long lectures every weekday starting at 9am, 10am, 11am, noon, 2pm, 3pm and 4pm. He asked how many lectures I had.

"You're not going to believe this," I began.

He didn't.

I felt uneasy. For my last few years at school I'd partly fought against and partly succumbed to the peer-group notion that it was cool not to do any work while the teachers were telling us to do more: and now, in my first educational experience as an adult, this had all been reversed.

Anyway, I was a good student and did all my weekly essays. Eighteen months passed and the week arrived when we historians were about to take our Part Ones at the end of the second year. Every other faculty did theirs at the end of the first year which allowed less time to screw up. However, I felt pretty confident.

A few days before the first exam, I ran into my friend Sean who was doing the same papers as me. "Brian, Brian," he said, "look – just tell me something about Otto the Great."

I swelled slightly. I knew quite a lot about Otto the Great, a very significant figure in medieval German history. What did Sean need to know? His motives during the Rebellion of the Dukes? His role in the Ottonian Renaissance? His relationship with the Papacy, the Slavs or the Byzantine Empire? His Charlemagne complex?

"Yes, yes," he interrupted me. "All I want to know is…"

"Yes?"

"Look – was he French or German?"

We both got the same grade, which briefly pissed me off.

Another year rolled by and finals approached. Anglo-Norman Feudalism – not a phrase you read every day – was one of my papers. A few weeks before the balloon went up I met George on the bridge in the middle of the college. George was also a historian and also studying this paper. He was vastly cleverer than me. He had this way with him, as many very clever people have, of fixing a half-smile on his face when listening to what you were saying in which surprise, contempt and disappointment were mixed in roughly equal measure.

That expression was there when I answered his first question, whether I'd read a 20-page article with the snappy title of *Politics & Property in Medieval England* by JC Holt. I told him I had but that I hadn't understood it.

"No," he said, "I don't suppose you did."

Even George, not the most empathetic of men, must have seen from my expression that this was going a bit far. "I didn't understand it the first time either," he grudgingly admitted.

"How many times did you read it before you did?"

"Three. You need to read it again, and again, and again. Read it until you understand it. Don't bother about anything else. When you understand it you will understand everything. Nothing else matters. If you understand it you'll get a first in that paper at least. If you don't you won't."

If I'd climbed a Himalayan peak to learn the secret of life and the universe from a aged savant I couldn't have hoped for clearer advice. I followed it to the letter. I got a copy of the article and read it six more times without success.

Then I read it for the seventh time and I got it.

I can't, after this passage of time, tell you what 'it' was, not exactly. There are no facts or examples I can now recall to describe this epiphany. The closest I can come is to say that it was like seeing and understanding the complex and interconnected workings of a watch, or standing on a mountaintop and having the mist suddenly clear so that the whole landscape lay spread before me. George had been right. It all made sense. No intellectual achievement since has come close to that moment. The entire business of my being at university at all was vindicated. I paid no further attention to any revision for this topic, fearful that one more fact might shatter my insight which was, I suspected, probably pretty fragile. Three days later I went into the exam and duly, in that paper, got a first.

There were four other papers. The one I'd marked down as my banker for my best marks was on the Crusades. I was particularly fascinated by the Fourth Crusade of 1204, one of those bizarre events which show just how badly fate can wreck the best-laid plans. The expedition never left Europe, sacked two Christian cities and conquered Constantinople. By the end most of the army had been excommunicated. It was the spiritual equivalent of an AA group going on a drunken rampage and stealing the crown jewels. I knew a fair bit about it and had a reasonably original theory about what had been going on. All I needed was a question, any question, on this event. I had established from past papers that one always came up. Judge for yourself my disappointment when I found no such question there.

There were fewer questions to choose from than I'd expected, only ten rather than about 17, which should have given me a clue as to what was going on. I chose my three essays, spent an hour on each, and finished the last with a few minutes to spare. As I was collecting my sheets together the exam paper fell on the floor and landed the other side up. There were seven more questions there, including one on the Fourth Crusade. I'd forgotten to turn the paper over.

At no time since has anyone asked me to tell them about the Fourth Crusade. I've told a few people, unbidden, usually failing to notice that glazed, twitchy expression that only deep boredom can engender. I don't think that perfect theory is there any more. Nor could I tell you a great deal about Anglo-Norman feudalism nor my old friend Otto the Great. As for turning over pieces of paper, only a few weeks ago I had to fill out and post off a form and a week later it came back with a note telling me there were more sections on the back that I hadn't completed. Seems like that woman on the radio was right after all.

Stiff Upper Lip

UNLIKE MOST OF the population I'm completely uninterested in genealogy, mine or anyone else's. I can understand the fascination but I can't share it. All I know about my own ancestors is that my paternal grandfather in Dublin was the first person to put Guinness in half-pint bottles; while, on my mother's side, my grandfather was 58 years old and my grandmother 17 when they got married. In their Devon village this seemed to have attracted no opprobrium. He was the local GP and so it was regarded as being a good match. If a 58-year-old GP tried to pull that stunt with one of his patients now he'd be struck off. That aside, I know nothing about my forebears and am happy to leave it that way.

Given this indifference, it's therefore odd that several of the jobs I've had have involved genealogy or genealogists in some form. There was another one that might have been added to this list.

This farcical event took place in the early 1980s. I was just out of university and starting to realise that a history degree was not the passport to wealth and happiness I'd somehow hoped. I was living in a freezing, rat-infested flat in Vauxhall and spending most of my time playing guitar, cadging pints and getting fired from a succession of jobs in pubs and warehouses. Money was running out. Something needed to be done. The shades of Thatcher's Britain were drawing in: the miner's strike was looming; Brixton was in flames; discord was stalking the land. I was contributing next to nothing to this rapidly changing world and, more immediately, in danger of contributing nothing at all to the landlord's next rent demand.

It's possible all this had started to unhinge my mind. Certainly I can find no other explanation for why I decided to write a letter to

Debrett's asking them for a job. I cannot imagine why I chose this company, nor what career path I thought it might lead me to, nor how this would square with my unfocussed bohemian lifestyle. However, any misgivings I had were obliterated when, a few days later, I received a very civil reply inviting me to attend an interview at their offices in Winchester at one o'clock the following Saturday. Matters were now out my hands. I'd asked for it: now I had to go.

My good intentions of spending Friday evening soberly at home ironing my shirt and researching this firm I had so spontaneously contacted vanished in the face of a party invite that seemed, as they always do, too good to miss.

Saturday morning found me slightly shaky and hunting for something suitable to wear. When I looked in the mirror I realised that nothing quite matched and that the whole effect was wrong, regardless of what job I was applying for. Then I sensed something else was wrong. Ah, yes – I needed to shave.

All went well with the new razor until I tried to do that tricky bit just above the top lip. I briefly stopped concentrating. A few seconds later two identical and deep cuts had opened up just where my lip met the skin. Blood flowed freely, some of it onto my shirt. I had no other shirt.

There is almost no part of the body more impossible to apply a sticking plaster to than the top lip. I ran it under the cold tap for several minutes, trying to clean the shirt at the same time. The results, when I next dared look in the mirror, were not encouraging. My tie, if positioned at a certain and rather artificial angle, would hide the worst of the bloodstains on the shirt but nothing short of a full-face mask was going to hide the cut on the lip. There was also a wildness about my eyes that didn't jive with the suave impression I would soon be trying to create. My hair was standing on end but as I didn't own a hairbrush there was nothing I could do about that. Time was moving on. The train left in half an hour.

I don't know how well you know Waterloo station. Now it's just like any other London terminus, all Costa coffee shops and clear digital signage. In the early 80s it was a human zoo. Nothing, bar nothing, was more squalid and disorganised than any British Rail station at this time. Waterloo was one of the worst, the station and the area around it being a kind of unofficial homeless shelter, opium den and post-pub fight club. It being Saturday morning, there were plenty of of dazed and crusty-looking folk who'd been out in the clubs til god-knows-when and were now trying to fare-dodge a ride back to the sticks. Many looked as if they'd spent part of the night being beaten up by the police and some probably had. Surrounded by all this, you might think that I would have passed unnoticed. Not a bit of it. The ticket collector was so shocked by my appearance that he didn't want to let me on the train.

For someone going to an interview with Debrett's this was an unexpected obstacle. People who could barely stand upright were allowed to pass unhindered. I finally convinced him that I wasn't going to die on the journey or start a fight and took my seat in the carriage. Fortunately I was alone. I had quite a bit of work to do.

The first thing was to try to staunch the wound. Jabbing at it with the sheets of paper I'd brought with me was, I now saw, re-opening the cut as fast as I was mopping up the blood. Time, that would be the great healer. I didn't, however, have a lot of it. I spent the next half an hour with my mouth motionless, from time to time licking droplets of blood from my lip. As we neared Winchester I sensed the cut was closing. Careful experimentation, interrupted once by a surprised ticket collector, suggested that some form of speech would be possible as long as I exhibited no emotion of any kind and as long as I avoided any consonants that would make my lip bend. Further research suggested that words containing b, m, p, qu, tr, v and w would cause problems. This ruled out a sizeable chunk of the English language, including my name, but I would just have to make do with the rest. I was no longer bleeding. The sun was shining. Everything was going to be fine.

Once in Winchester I discovered that the offices were only five minutes' walk from the station and that it was only just twenty past twelve. The obvious solution, or so it seemed at the time, was to have a drink, which I felt I'd earned. I turned into a pub and ordered – perhaps out of subconscious deference to my grandfather – a half of Guinness. I raised it to my lips.

Two things happened almost immediately. The first was that the cut re-opened; the second was that, as my mouth briefly stopped working to cope with this new emergency, most of the Guinness cascaded down the front of my shirt. I went straight into the gents to effect some repairs and was genuinely shocked by the apparition that greeted me in the mirror. The mixture of blood and Guinness on a white shirt is impossible to disguise but I reckoned that by keeping by jacket pulled tightly around my chest I could conceal the sight, if perhaps not the smell. Blood was once more flowing freely from the cut, my Trappist behaviour on the train reduced to naught. The dirty shoes, the odd socks, the sticking-up hair and, as I saw now for the first time, the fact that I hadn't properly shaved the left side of my face would have to take care of themselves. I looked at my watch. Ten-to. Destiny called.

The woman at the reception was very pleasant. Good afternoon Mr Quinn, we are expecting you: please take a seat. The office beyond her was largely open-plan. Half a dozen other people were working. A few minutes later, a middle-aged man made his way over. The receptionist nudged her colleague. Both turned to us with what I thought was a disproportionate level of interest.

I'd been spending the time running over some likely sentences, looking for obvious obstacles. The matter of what I was going to get asked and what I might reply had become irrelevant. My ambition had shrunk to considering only what I could actually pronounce.

"This is Mr Taylor ," the woman said. She seemed to be supressing some emotion. "He'll be interviewing you."

Mr Taylor shook my hand. Greetings were exchanged. He led me to a desk in the middle of the office. I was aware of the other workers stopping what they were doing and turning their attention towards us.

"So, Mr Quinn, thank you for coming to see us," he began. The words came out as smooth as you like, his lips perfectly forming every syllable.

'Thank you for seeing me," I said carefully.

"So…" He sat back in the chair. "Why would you like to work for Debr-bre-bre-bre…" With every stammered sound a spray of saliva shot itself from his mouth and onto the pointless notepad that lay on the desk between us. "…for us?" he asked at last.

For a moment I couldn't speak at all. "Because I feel," I began; then realised that too much emotion had been put into 'feel', so re-opening the cut. "Excuse me," I said, and dabbed at my mouth with some tissue paper. Would now be a good time to explain about how I'd injured myself? Probably not, as I was halfway through answering an interview question. What had the question been? I couldn't remember. What the hell was I doing here, anyway?

"Excuse me," I said again, a faint spray of blood coming from my mouth.

"N-n-n-n-ot at-at-at all," he said, a faint spray of saliva coming from his.

We stared slightly wildly at each other. I was still aware of the attentiveness in the rest of the office as all eyes and ears were glued to this extraordinary conversation.

I tried to pick up the thread of my remarks. "Because I feel that…" What did I feel, exactly? I had now no idea what I was trying to say. "I feel that it would be interesting."

Mr Taylor nodded slowly as if I'd just said something profound.

"Indeed, yes. It can be very int-tr-tr-tr-tersting because it-it-it-it…"

We struggled on for a bit longer but neither of us had the strength or stamina to keep it up. His stammer seemed to be triggered by many of the same letters and sounds that I was trying myself to avoid: no great consolation for him, I suspect. I have no recollection of what we talked about. My next clear memory was of him asking what my travel costs had been. Why was he asking me that?

"Eleven pounds," I said at last. It had been twelve, but I couldn't say 'twelve. If Mr Taylor couldn't say 'interesting' then he probably couldn't say 'twelve', either. All in all, it was a word best avoided: that and so many others.

He reached into a drawer and counted out the money. "Thank you again for coming to see us," he said. He was the politest man I'd ever met. "We'll be in t-t-t-t-t-t…we'll write."

I nodded. There seemed nothing else to say.

I didn't get the job. Another civil letter followed a few days later thanking me for my interest blah blah, but on this occasion blah blah, we wish you every success in your future career.

The unfortunate episode taught me an important lesson. If I have to be somewhere looking smart I always shave the night before. As advice goes it's perhaps not that profound but, believe me, it's well worth bearing in mind.

As for the charming, polite Mr Taylor, I felt genuine sorrow. I was back to normal speech within a few hours: for him, his stammer, which prevented his even pronouncing the name of the company he worked for and probably deeply loved – and perhaps also his own surname – would follow him every day of his life. How he had been persuaded to conduct an interview was beyond me. Nor did he ever manage to share with me why he thought genealogy was interesting. He may have had an excellent point but I never learned what it was. It's his secret and as far as I'm concerned he can keep it.

Leaving Las Vegas

EVERY SO OFTEN, usually in the letters pages of newspapers, the question of national service rears its head. I don't want to open up that bag of snakes here except to say that, each time, I ask myself what the purpose of any compulsory activity ought to be. National service, whatever form that service takes, is expensive and has aims whose success can't easily be measured. It also seems designed to encourage a particular attitude. Better, perhaps, might be something that discourages or warns, using shock-aversion tactics.

I once visited someone in a high-security prison. It was one of the most horrible experiences of my life. I've often thought that if, at 18, everyone had to spend 48 hours in one then crime rates would halve. You could add other places to your list and, when your turn at ruling the country comes round, put them into action. For example, we're often told how bad air travel is for the environment. Two days hanging around Heathrow would, at an impressionable age, put many people off this mode of transport for life.

Of course, many feel that the real problems in the world are the economic and political systems which we all have to endure. How can the extremes be experienced? It's impractical to organise for every 18-year-old to spend two days at a Chinese Communist Party conference, in a Trappist monastery or on the streets of Mogadishu. In any case, would this really put them off communism, Roman Catholicism or anarchy? Are these even desirable goals?

Easier to encounter is capitalism, the system under which we live and which is – to adjust Churchill's remark about democracy – the worst system of all, apart from all the others. Like any system, it's led to some spectacular excesses; and it's against those that we need to warn our young people. It is therefore my pledge that, if ever I become Prime Minister, I shall make it a legal obligation for every person to spend at least 48 hours in Las Vegas (with 24 hours in Los Angeles as a recommended extra) before their 25th birthday. This will show just how far capitalism – and in particular conspicuous consumption and the hopeless pursuit of easy money – can go if left to its own devices.

Penny and I went there about 20 years ago on the last leg of a US east-west road trip. One remarkable thing about the journey was that we got from Greenwich Village to Knoxville TN – about 750 miles – on the first day, something I don't think even Kerouac on speed could have managed. The fifth day saw us driving across the desert towards the gaudy, neon-lit 24/7 shrine to the American dream. Most of what I knew about Vegas was based on a few movies and Hunter S. Thompson's alarming *Fear and Loathing*. In some ways, the reality was even odder.

In fact, I knew one other thing, based on a story told to me a few years before by someone who was an travel agent who organised trips for companies to incentivise and reward their staff. He'd set his company up on, let's say, 1 May. On 3 May he'd had a phone call from a steel factory in Sunderland saying that the place had beaten its target for the year and that the reward was a long weekend in Las Vegas. Could he quote? He did, and got the gig.

"How many people?" I asked. I was expecting seventy; perhaps a hundred or so tops.

"Two thousand four hundred," he replied with slow relish. He paused to let this sink in. "That's about six jumbo jets."

I thought about this for a moment, trying to imagine what this would involve. I wasn't surprised when he told me that he didn't sleep at all for three days before the trip and hardly at all during it. "Then," he added, "there was the business of the beer."

"The beer?"

"I used to think that the phrase 'drinking the town dry of beer' was just an expression," he said. "But it actually happened to us." He stared into his own beer and shook his head in wonderment. "They *drank Las Vegas dry*. Can you imagine?"

I couldn't. Nor could I decently ask him how much he'd made out of the deal. Whatever it was, it couldn't have been nearly enough.

Penny and I had more modest expectations: but Vegas doesn't deal in modesty. Nothing about the place, at least the area round The Strip, could be called reserved or understated. At that time, the city had seven of the world's ten largest hotels. We picked one at random. It was vast in every respect. The first surprise was how cheap the room was, about $20. This, too, was on a super-human scale, with a massive TV, huge windows and a bed large enough to have comfortably accommodated four people, which was perhaps a regular requirement. The view from the window was of even larger hotels and, beyond them, the vastness of the desert and the empty, cloudless sky. Everything was designed to challenge and undermine a normal sense of proportion. Humans were reduced to physical insignificance: all that mattered was how much money they had in their pockets.

We got changed and went out to hit the town.

Gambling has never interested me very much – I've only been into a bookie's twice and never visited a casino – but to go to Las Vegas without sampling the million-and-one games of pre-arranged chance that have been assembled for your entertainment is like driving to the Grand Canyon (which we'd done the previous day) and not getting out of the car. Later that evening, on returning to the hotel after a couple of hours strolling up and down The Strip, we didn't dare venture anywhere near the roulette tables but instead found ourselves in a vast cathedral of slot machines with various bars set off it, like chapels.

Here we made an interesting discovery, unique in my experience of licensed premises: as long as you continued to put money into the table-top slot machines – which played a strange kind of Hold'em poker – you didn't have to pay for your drinks. Penny soon tired of this entertainment and went to bed. For me, the lure of free beer was irresistible. An hour later I'd played fifteen hands of poker against the machine. I'd won four bucks in tokens on one hand and lost the other fourteen. Each game cost, I think, a dollar. I'd had perhaps six beers, which might normally have cost, say, two dollars each. I was therefore pretty even. As I stood up I realised that I was also pretty pissed.

The next two minutes were a bit of a nightmare. It became important to cash in the tokens at the desk in the centre of the hall at the big 'Cash-in' sign above to show that I'd got something from the evening. However, someone far cleverer than me had created a maze of huge slot machines which made reaching it impossible. It was *Alice Through the Looking Glass* re-written by Hunter S. Thompson. At each turn of the labyrinth I was confronted by a cul-de-sac filled with steely-eyed gamblers, mostly of above middle age, single-mindedly setting themselves to beat the machine they were stationed at. These dens of pleasure had been designed to create a sense of timelessness. There were no clocks. There was no natural light. The building was continuously refreshed with oxygen-rich air at a carefully calculated temperature. These aspects were all designed to keep the punters awake and alert: perhaps even alive.

Suddenly, finding my way to this grail seemed like too much trouble What was four dollars, anyway? If I couldn't get to the desk to cash them in, that was just the way it was here. I paused by one brightly flashing machine and obediently put my first token in the inviting slot. Vegas had beaten me.

With no sense of what I was doing, I inserted the tokens one by one and pressed the huge flashing button. The fourth time there was one of those *ker-ching!* noises that I'd only previously heard in the movies. A cascade of coins rattled into the tray. I could just about fit them into my cupped hands. I had no difficulty finding the cash desk after that.

"That's eighty-five dollars," the perky young woman at the desk said, pushing the notes across. "Have a nice day." It was probably about two in the morning.

I managed to find the room and staggered into bed. "We're rich!" I slurred to Penny. "Mmph," she replied.

The next day we woke surprisingly early and I told her about my good fortune. We agreed we needed to get out of this place as soon as possible and claim what was probably a fairly rare record of departing Las Vegas in possession of more money than we'd arrived with. We packed and ate breakfast in the cavernous dining room and then, as it was still only eight o'clock, decided to have a cooling swim in the hotel pool before leaving. We had a long day's drive ahead of us.

Despite the baking heat we were the only people there apart from a young man cleaning leaves from the surface of the water. Like everything in this town, the pool was of an outlandish shape that made length swimming impossible but we splashed about for twenty minutes before getting out. The water tasted strange; not the normal acrid odour of chlorine but something more herbal, almost like mown grass. I commented on this to the man who rattled off some long name which started 'bromo'. He seemed very proud of it: it was the latest thing, he assured us, effective and harmless.

Fifteen minutes later we were driving out of town on the last leg of our trip heading west to LA.

The journey was about 270 miles, the first part across the Mojave Desert to Barstow after which, or so it seemed from the map, the landscape became slightly less forbidding. All I knew of Barstow was that it was mentioned in the first line of *Fear and Loathing in Las Vegas*: "We were somewhere near Barstow on the edge of the desert when the drugs began to take hold." In our case they took hold rather sooner, in fact about fifteen minutes out of Vegas.

At first I thought it was haze or mist, which seemed odd in the clear, hot desert air.

"Can you see that blur?" I asked Penny. She could. We drove on. The mist got worse.

After another half a mile we both realised that the mist was not coming from outside the car but from inside our eyes. It was an alarming moment. As it was happening to both of us at the same time we thought it must be a chemical in the air though, if so, the other drivers seemed to be having no problem with it. Mercifully, a motel appeared on the left and we pulled in, parked and sat blinking at each other like a pair of moles. We finally realised it must have been the bromo-whatsit in the pool. The Las Vegas skyline was still visible behind us, in as much as anything was visible. After about forty minutes our eyesight started to return to normal and we set off again. Las Vegas had tried to trap us but, marginally in profit, we'd escaped. Many others had been less fortunate. Some may be trapped there yet.

Later that afternoon I'd have given anything to be back on The Strip. We were on a hellish six-lane LA beltway, driving into a vast setting sun. Traffic was overtaking on both sides. Confusingly-signed interchanges were coming at us every minute or so but were perilous to reach because of the quaint US preference for having the entry slip roads join the freeway just before the exit ones leave it. All this was happening at 70mph and, so far as we were concerned, on the wrong side of the road. We had no idea of where we were meant to turn off nor even where we were, our large-scale map of the USA now useless. Our eyes were also starting to go weird again. I'd like to pretend that we maintained a calm and dignified affability towards each other. I'd be lying.

When, by a series of miracles, we found the street we were bound for we were still arguing. I reversed into the drive, knocking over a dustbin, and brought the car to a shuddering, stalling stop inches from the garage door. Wild-eyed and dishevelled we got out. A man was standing by the front door: our un-met host for the next four days. It was his garage, his dustbin and his car that we'd been driving across the country. Fortunately there was no obvious damage.

"You must be Penny and Brian," he said dryly. "Welcome to LA. It's a beautiful city!"

We did our best to agree, although the first impressions weren't encouraging. My overwhelming feeling, as we staggered indoors in the (unfulfilled) hope of being offered a cold beer, was that we'd spent the day fleeing one madhouse only to find ourselves trapped in another one. We'd only just escaped Vegas. I can't pretend we had had the nightmares Hunter S Thomson endured, but all problems are relative. As for escaping LA, we had return plane tickets in our pockets. Four days there gave me no reason to change my view of the place. If I never go back to either city it will be too soon. Still, we saw them, which was the object of the exercise. My view of capitalism hasn't been quite the same since.

So, yes, I repeat my earlier advice: if you've never been to either Vegas or LA, go, and see what the market economy is like when the brakes are taken off. But remember to take some swimming goggles and don't arrive in LA in the rush hour. That's the only advice I can give you. Apart from that, I'm afraid you're on your own. That's what capitalism is all about, right?

The Flaming Telephone

EVERYONE HAS THEIR own story about destruction, outrageous behaviour and chaos at a Christmas party. This is mine.

The reason I'm able to remember it so clearly is because I was about nine at the time. Even by the rather dissipated standards of my parents' social life, it was far from a normal evening.

For the first hour or so I wandered around, occasionally talking to people (probably in that awful precocious way that some nine-year-olds, including this one, have when allowed to mix with adults) and eating huge amounts of cake. This seemed to be the only food my mother had organised. Always quite a haphazard hostess, she'd also invited just about everyone she knew and, she later admitted, quite a few people she didn't. There was plenty to drink but, apart from cake, nothing to eat. No real drink-driving laws at that time – particularly not in rural France, where this took place – and within an hour or so everyone was roaring drunk.

My father later tried to justify the whole fiasco by saying that the temperature change between the cold outdoors and the hot house had been responsible for everyone's disorganised behaviour. Even at the time I thought that this was a pretty feeble excuse.

One early conversation I remember was with three people who were talking about mescaline, of which I'd never heard. I repeated it back as 'masculine', which seemed to make almost as much sense. They laughed at me: one patted me on the head. I stored the word away in my mind, vowing to look it up and, the next time, to use it correctly. When I did, a few months later, my parents were shocked. I delighted in telling them where I'd first heard it. What an appalling little boy I must have been.

About half an hour later I had a ring-side seat for something that I thought only happened in silly comedy films. A man was pouring red wine but paying far too much attention to the woman he was talking to. The bottle and the glass were not aligned and I watched with delighted fascination as almost all the wine cascaded not into the glass but onto the yellow sofa on which they were sitting. When he realised what he'd done he stood up, dropping the bottle, and stepped against a low coffee table, breaking one of the legs.

This didn't matter as much as it might have done as about five minutes later someone fell across the table, smashing it into several pieces. The floor was tiled so the noise, including the disintegration of the glass, was particularly effective to my young ears. By now the noise was so intense and the room so crowded that it probably passed unnoticed by anyone not directly involved. Not unnoticed by me, however: I was drinking up these sensations with as much delight as the guests were drinking their wine and whisky. Unlike them, I was also able to remember them.

The undoubted highlight of the early part of the evening was when the telephone caught fire. It was on a tall bread cupboard on the far side of the room from where I was standing so, once again, I had a fine view. Next to it were some candleholders that were, for reasons known only to the manufacturer, made of what turned out to be flammable plastic. The four candles had burnt down and melted the holder, which dribbled over the phone: then, the whole concoction of Bakelite, plastic and candle wax erupted. The flames were, as I remember, greeny-yellow, accompanied by a pleasingly dense little cloud of black smoke. Someone poured white wine over it, the phone was salvaged, everything else was thrown away and the party continued, most of the guests not missing a beat.

At some other time in my early childhood, my father – who could be very amusing when the mood was on him – told a story so funny that it made his hostess laugh with such abandon that her trousers fell down. That has always existed for me as the standard by which a good story should be judged, one I've never achieved myself. In the same way, when someone describes a particularly dissipated party, I'm often tempted to ask, 'ah – but did the telephone catch fire?'

I still have the bread cupboard. Years ago I managed only at the last minute to stop my then partner from having the burn mark removed by a French polisher. It's a tangible sign of my past. Every so often I run my finger over it and recall that evening, and my childhood in general: a time when splintered tables, wrecked sofas and flaming telephones were sources of delight and not, as they would be to most adult hosts, reasons for simmering or explosive rage.

In fact, I don't think my mother was that bothered by all these disasters. As for my father, by this time he'd had enough and had gone up onto the roof terrace where we had a small telescope on a tripod. After a while, I joined him. My most tranquil recollection of the evening is being up there with him in the clear, cold, dark night. Two floors below, the noise of the party could be heard, mainly as a dull rumble like an approaching goods train but interspersed with staccato yelps, whoops of laughter and the occasional crash of breaking glass. We meanwhile, were eating chocolate cake and looking at the rings around Saturn, two occupations not normally associated with each other.

Like all good parties, the best moment was saved until last.

It must by this time have been about two in the morning. All the guests had gone, apart from one man passed out under the dining table. My mother was sitting on a low chair, taking in the full extent of the devastation. My father, whose idea the party had not been, had an 'I told you so' expression on his face that he was wise enough not to put into words. The only other person was someone who was staying with us. She decided that this was the moment when she could contribute something really useful. Despite my mother's feeble protests that 'it was better left until the morning,' she went round the room, putting the glasses on a large tray.

The tray probably held twenty or so glasses and, when it was full, she started towards the kitchen. I've already said that the floors were tiled. It would also help if I explained that there were two steps that led from the living room up to the kitchen on the far side of the hall. My mother could tell that the guest was in no state to attempt such a journey and made another attempt to stop her. 'No, no – 's leasht I can do' was the reply.

I think my mother shut her eyes at this point.

The well-meaning guest felt forward with her foot and made it to the first step. The second took her completely by surprise. There was a wonderful moment when everything – her, the tray and all the glasses – were in mid-air: then the whole lot landed. The noise was indescribable.

The tearful, confused apologies and insincere 'it really doesn't matter' and 'it's nothing' from my mother made me – and I suspect my father – cower away in embarrassment. When we turned back it was to witness an even more grotesque scene, with the weeping guest now trying to pick up the million pieces of broken glass by hand. Did she cut herself? Of course she did. Bandages; plasters; more tears; more apologies; more assurances that the whole thing didn't matter in the slightest. This seemed like a good moment to go to bed.

My parents hardly ever referred to the evening again. Looking back on it, this rather surprises me, The way I see it, a party at which a telephone bursts into flames is an event to cherish. Whenever I rest my fingers on the scar on the top of the bread cupboard and close my eyes, I can sometimes almost feel the heat from the scorched wood; if I strain my imagination, I can also almost hear the splintering of the table, the glug-glug of the red wine soaking into the yellow sofa and – best of all – the magical noise made by twenty wine glasses disintegrating on a Provençal tiled floor.

Releasing my Inner Yak

SO THERE WE were, Penny and I and Penny's cousin in his house in Normandy, drinking coffee and watching the rain lash almost horizontally against the window panes. Lunch – an event I always look forward to in France – was to be taken in a nearby town in an hour or so. A walk seemed out of the question. There was one other option. Penny suggested that we each draw a mandala.

A mandala is, as it was explained to me, a symmetrical decorative pattern usually in the form of a circle: a kind of formally structured doodle. Its origins and purposes are, of course, more sophisticated.

We looked it up. One website said that it was originally a Sanskrit word which 'represents wholeness; a model for the organisational structure of life itself; a cosmic diagram to remind us of our relation to the infinite, the world that extends beyond and within our bodies and minds.' Another went further still, explaining that it can 'help you gain wisdom and transmit positive energies to the environment to create a healing power': this can extend, believe it or not, 'to the whole world.'

Let's do it, I said. If even just one of these things resulted it would surely go down as a good morning's work. There are many less edifying things one can get up to on a rainy Sunday than transmitting a healing power to the whole world. I could hardly wait to get started.

Penny explained that mandalas are sometimes created using coloured sand. Once completed, the artwork is then swept up, so reminding us of the transience of worldly concerns. This moral seemed worth bearing in mind but I pointed out that we didn't have any coloured sand. Even if we were to find or make some it might cause a bit of a mess but I didn't mention this: two minutes with the hoover seemed a small price to pay for all the other benefits on offer.

"You can do it with coloured pencils as well," Penny said. John produced a pot of them. She neatly tore some A4 sheets into squares. We were good to go.

I don't know why it is but normally when you're confronted with a set of coloured pencils, no matter how many there are, there are no red ones. Where do they go? If you don't believe me, empty out the pot or box of coloured pencils that all homes have and count how many reds there are. See what I mean?

On this occasion the situation was otherwise. Out of the sixty or so pencils in the box at least fifteen were red of some kind, ranging from coral pink to deep crimson. What's more, all the reds were gathered together with a rubber band. It seemed a good omen. We set to work.

Penny is an excellent artist. John seemed competent as well. The only thing I can draw is an elephant from the back, though I usually have to explain to people afterwards what it is. As a preparatory flourish I executed one of these (in red) and presented to my host. I also signed it – you never know.

Drawing a mandala involves developing and repeating a pattern four times, each one at a 90-degree angle. This was easy when I started, and proved easy throughout for the other two, but soon my pattern started to veer off in a way which threatened to undermine the sense of harmony and balance the exercise was designed to accomplish. I do some things more comfortably with my right hand and some with my left. After a while I switched over the pencil from left to right but it made no appreciable difference to the results. At least my incompetence was balanced even if my angles weren't.

After a while a sense of calm overcame me. I was now colouring in the various shapes, attempting to apply some symmetry to this task as well. The activity made no demands on my intellect and, as I have no pretensions to being able to draw, none on my self-respect.

Ten minutes later it was finished. The results were rather pleasing, if only because they had flowed unbidden down variously my left arm and my right and onto the paper in a way which if not technically accomplished was at least spontaneous.

I felt unexpectedly satisfied. I had been granted a short period of tranquil detachment with, beyond it, perhaps the briefest glimpse of a temple shimmering in the Himalayan snows.

"There we go," I said, tossing my sheet into the middle of the table. "I've released my inner yak." This announcement was greeted with polite congratulations. My effort looked kindergarten. Theirs more resembled preliminary sketches for the ceiling of the Sistine Chapel. Still, my yak was out: that was what mattered.

Then over-confidence kicked in. I decided to use a ruler to trim off the parts of the paper to which my design hadn't extended. As often happens, something that kind of works when you're following instinct or emotion goes all to hell when you begin thinking about it. The first three cuts went fine. On the fourth my hand slipped and I tore the whole sheet from one corner to the other.

Was my recently-released inner yak constrained or harmed as a result? Not a bit of it. Remembering the lesson of the monks who obliterated their hours of careful sand-art with a few strokes of a broom, I faced the transience of my creation head-on. I screwed up the two pieces of paper and threw them in the bin.

Feeling much refreshed, we then went out to lunch.

The following day on the way back to the ferry we stopped off in Falaise in search of a good restaurant I remembered from a previous visit. Falaise was the birthplace of William the Conqueror, a man as far removed from any Buddhist sentiments as I can think of. Judge then of my surprise and delight when we saw a circus setting up in a park and, tethered to a post nearby, a yak calmly contemplating the castle battlements.

"That's my yak," I said to Penny. "The one I released."

"So it is," she replied.

I slowed down and studied the yak more closely. Although I have no standard by which to judge a yak's reactions to its circumstances, it appeared to be perfectly content. Our gazes – his ruminative, mine inquisitive – might briefly have met. Then, pleased that some small circle in the mandala of my own life seemed to have been closed, I changed down gear and went on my way rejoicing.

In Which we Discover what Pooh & Piglet Do in the Evenings

IT RAINED AND it rained and it rained. Piglet was goodness knows how old – he couldn't remember because Christopher Robin had never told him, but he certainly felt old enough this morning – and he'd never seen so much rain. Not a good start to the day.

He flicked the curtains shut and groped his way across the room. Standing on tip-toe he managed to switch on the light.

"Christ, turn that bloody thing off," said a growly voice from under a pile of rugs on the bed.

"Good morning, Pooh," Piglet said, in a nervous little voice. When Pooh was in One Of His Moods, Piglet became nervous. He was, after all and in every way, A Very Small Animal.

"Grumph," said Pooh. Piglet went into the kitchen, piled high with dirty plates, bottles and honey pots, and started nosing around in the cupboard, looking for coffee and aspirin. After a while he heard a thump on the floor, a curse and a cough. Winne-the-Pooh had got up.

A few moments later Pooh himself was in the kitchen, crashing around as usual. Piglet stepped back, not wanting to get squished.

"My God, what a night," Pooh said: "My *head*. We'd better get ourselves straightened out. Where's that coffee? He's going to be here any minute to take us off on some madcap adventure."

Neither of them could tell the time because, being animals of supposedly Very Little Brains, Christopher Robin had not seen fit to teach them. Pooh's clock was, of course, no help. But, being animals, They Knew.

Pooh jammed some beans into the grinder but as usual his paws didn't manage to screw the top down before he switched it on. Piglet reached up and took it off him just in time. His trotters, though hardly more dexterous, were at least smaller. Ignoring Pooh's theatrical grimaces at the noise, he managed to get the beans ground and the coffee percolating without too many mishaps. He never understood where all the things in his, and Pooh's, and Kanga's and all the rest of their kitchens came from. Most of the items were virtually unusable without an opposable thumb or, in Owl's case, hands. It seemed that the world had been designed for creatures other than them. That was just The Way Things Were. He also wondered why he sometimes thought in capital letters. Another thing he ought to ask Mr Milne, though he knew he'd never have the courage to do so.

"Wonder what Twinkle-toes has got planned for us today?" Pooh grumbled. Piglet stiffened slightly, not that anyone would have noticed. Christopher Robin was their friend, their protector. He was God. In the evenings – yes, in the evenings, when they were on their own, their baser animal instincts might be excused: but during the day, they were his playthings. It was The Way It Was. It upset him to hear Pooh speaking so roughly about him, the more so as Pooh would never dare to do so to his face.

He passed Pooh some coffee and sat down at the table, his little trotters curled around the egg-cup that he used for his Americanos.

Pooh took his coffee over to the window and started to roll a cigarette, with predictably disastrous results. He sucked at it for a few moments before a final defiant puff made the whole thing explode. "Of course, I *love* him," Pooh said tiredly, "but sometimes, you know, he's a bit too bloody cheerful." He stared moodily at the remains of his roll-up, some of which was now floating in his coffee. "Particularly first thing in the morning."

Piglet cocked his head at an unseen signal that was floating through the ether towards them. Pooh heard it too. He rubbed his paws through the thick, honey-encrusted fur on top of his head. Piglet drained his coffee and jumped to the floor, bouncing up and down on his hind legs, Ready For Anything. Piglet looked at Pooh and watched Pooh's slow, gentle, good-natured and slightly dim smile that was his familiar public expression slowly dawning over his face. They both moved into the main room towards the front door. Piglet caught a glimpse of himself in Pooh's cracked mirror. He looked pink and frightened, but suspected that he always did.

They stood waiting, their ears still cocked. The signals were stronger. One minute to go. Pooh let out a small fart.

There was a ring on the bell. "Pooh? Pooh!" said a familiar voice. Pooh lumbered forward and opened the door. Christopher Robin rushed in and gave Pooh a huge hug. "The bestest bear in the world," he said. Pooh grunted slightly. Christopher Robin stood back and beamed at them both. "Hello Piglet," he said.

"H...hello," Piglet said, feeling the tips of his ears going pink.

Pooh glanced at the clock on the wall, permanently stuck at five to eleven. "I was just thinking," he said dreamily, "that it was Time For A Little Something..."

Christopher Robin laughed. "Silly Old Bear! Come on, we're going to go and see Rabbit and Eeyore!" Piglet eyed the rain slanting down outside and the puddles that were forming outside, into which A Very Small Animal could, if he were not careful, Tumble And Drown. However Christopher Robin was there, with a very cheerful pair of red Wellington Boots so everything would be all right. Anyway, it was Showtime.

So there the three of them were, tramping off in the rain into the Hundred Acre Wood for another day of fun. Christopher Robin was already laughing at Pooh, who was Starting A Hum, and at Piglet whose ears were getting pink again because he was afraid that he would have join in with his squeaky voice at the 'tiddley-tum' bits.

But what Christopher Robin didn't know was that in the evenings, when he had said his prayers and been tucked up in bed by Nanny, Pooh and Piglet would sneak back, sometimes to Pooh's house and sometimes to Piglet's, and get thoroughly pissed.

* * *

"The trouble is," Pooh said the previous evening, staring moodily into a half-empty glass, "there's naff-all to do in the Wood at night."

As they were at Piglet's house, they were drinking haycorn gin. When they were at Pooh's they drank honey vodka. There wasn't much to choose between them as the spirits came from the same still near Rabbit's House which they'd told him was for Christopher Robin's school lessons. It was then simply a question of adding some haycorns or a bit of honey, as the case may be. The last batch but one had made them both go blind for two days; another had left them hallucinating, leading Mr Milne to write a story which no one had been prepared to publish.

Pooh filled up his glass. "We could get some of the others to come over," he said, as he often did.

Piglet blanched slightly. The evening Tigger had come over to his house and drunk half a bottle of haycorn gin was one he preferred to forget. Eeyore's brush with strong liquor had briefly cheered him up but soon afterwards he'd burst into tears and run off into the night. Kanga hadn't touched a drop but had lectured them for half an hour before, enraged with Pooh's unexpected sarcasm, hopping home in a huff. The recent Owl-and-Rabbit soirée had been perhaps the most ghastly, both of them talking incessantly using Very Long Words before Owl had left having knocking over several pieces of furniture while demonstrating the Power Of His Dorsal Muscles and Rabbit had thrown up in Pooh's hatstand and passed out under the table.

Alcohol was, Piglet realised, a terrible thing. Being a Very Small

Animal he took Very Small Drinks: Pooh, on the other hand, knocked it back like nobody's business and often went off on rants that lasted for ten minutes at a time. Piglet often didn't listen. Still, as Pooh had said, what the hell else was there to do?

"The other thing about the Wood," Pooh went on, "is the lack of crumpet."

Piglet felt his ears pinken.

"There's Kanga," Pooh said after a long belch, "but that's it. I don't know about Rabbit's Friends and Relations, of course. Some of them may be female. Thing is, Kanga's not exactly Hollywood, is she?"

Piglet looked across the table. Pooh was not exactly Hollywood either, certainly not now, a great big drunk, blurry, fuzzy thing half collapsed on the Ottoman. Piglet's only intimate dealings with Kanga – when she had forcibly stripped and bathed him after their abortive attempt to kidnap Roo at the sandpit – had left him in a state of suppressed erotic confusion from which he had yet to recover. The thought of a sexually-charged Kanga bouncing all over him in her four-poster bed was one that he only entertained during these drunken evenings, and then briefly. A few minutes of that image could keep his fragile little libido going for a week. Seeing Kanga in the flesh the day after these visions made him almost faint with nerves. Sex, like alcohol, was best left to those with stronger constitutions.

"We're a bloody odd bunch, aren't we?" Pooh said half to himself. "I mean, where did we all *come* from? Where do we *belong*? Take you, Piglet..."

Piglet jumped slightly. "Me?" he squeaked.

"Yes. All I know about you is this uncle, Trespassers William. Who was he?"

Piglet didn't speak for a moment. His memories of Trespassers William were still very much unfinished business. Still, as Pooh had brought the subject up he could hardly avoid it. "He used to come over a lot...to see my mother. He wasn't really an uncle. I was just told to call him that."

Pooh nodded. "Strange kind of name," he said. "Why was he called that?"

"Because he was a burglar. He used to bring my mother some of the stuff he' stole. He spent a lot of time with us. I didn't like him." Piglet now found he couldn't stop. "And at night, when mum was asleep he used to...he used to come into...my..." Just as suddenly, he had now dried up. The memory seemed so horribly vivid – the cold, dark sty; the sickly, foetid smell of Trespassers' breath; the grunting and groaning. He shuddered.

Pooh, with rare tact, changed the subject onto himself. "Sounds like Mr Sanders," he said. "Whoever exactly *he* was. My step-father, apparently. My mother didn't talk about my real father. Then this fat old bore turned up, so we all 'lived under the name of Sanders' because my mother said it was more seemly. He was a right bastard. Hated me. He took off one day with everything we owned. Which wasn't much, but still. Then I ended up here, via a charity shop in Hastings."

"Oh," said Piglet, who could think of nothing else to say. There was a long silence.

"What about the rest of us? So, who arrived after us?"

"Rabbit...no, not Rabbit. Owl."

"Yes, that's right, Owl. He was rescued from a lab. Did you know that, Piglet?"

"I didn't know that, Pooh, no."

"Christopher Robin told me. They'd been doing experiments on him, using drugs to build up his dorsal muscles or his frontal lobes or something, and Mr Milne rescued him. Perhaps the experiments are why he talks in that extraordinary way. Then, as you say, there's Rabbit." Pooh shook his head sadly and poured some more gin for them both. "He was one of the survivors from the myxom...myxi...

mixmo...it was a disease and it killed most of the rabbits. Mr Milne found him and they rescued him as well." Pooh sat back in his chair. "There's something a bit rum about Rabbit, don't you think?

"How do you mean, rum, Pooh?"

"Well, all those 'friends and relations' as he calls them. All sounds a bit like your uncle Trespassers William, don't you think?"

Piglet hadn't, and was horrified. The thought of big fat Rabbit and, say, Small the beetle...mind you, Trespassers had been far, far bigger than Piglet and that hadn't stopped him. Piglet watched Pooh shift his bulk in the armchair opposite. There were times when he felt like a Very Small Animal and this was one of them.

"Eeyore was rescued as well, from a donkey sanctuary, obviously. As you can tell every time you talk to him, something pretty awful must have happened to him. Not that he ever mentions it." He smiled at Piglet in an encouraging if rather drunk way. "It's good to talk about these things, if you can."

Piglet nodded a few times but didn't trust himself to speak.

"Tigger, of course, is endangered, simple as that. On all the WWF lists. He came from some zoo, I think, after his mother died." Pooh threw another mangled roll-up into the flickering fire and stared gloomily at it for a few moments. "If he keeps on coming round and waking me up at six in the morning he's going to be a damn sight more endangered, I can tell you. And who else is there?"

"Kanga."

"Of course – Kanga, and dear little Roo." Pooh sat back and tried to cross his legs but they wouldn't. "She *says* that they come from Australia. *Anyone* could say that. *I*, for example, could say I came from Australia." Pooh looked across the table at Piglet in a rather blank way.

"Yes, Pooh, you *could* say that."

"They *might* have come from Australia. With names like that... then again, they might be illegal immigrants from...from..." Pooh tried to think of another country. "Brazil," he suggested at last.

"Oh."

Pooh poured the last of the gin into his glass, having privately decided that Piglet had had enough, which he had.

"We're a bunch of fuck ups and no mistake. Look at us. One way or another we've all come off the scrap heap. Hardly a parent between us. I mean, look at dirty old Trespassers and Mr Sanders and the absent Mr Kanga – I don't see any positive male role models there, do you? The fact is, little CR, and Mr M, took pity on us. Fine. Great. How long will that last? What happens when he gets bored with us? When he grows up? All those lessons in the afternoon…"

Piglet had for some weeks been thinking the same thing and now started to sniffle. Pooh who, drunk or sober, was a kind if not always tactful bear, reached across the table and patted Piglet's trotter. With the ghost of Trespassers so recently out of his box he felt that was about as much physical proximity as Piglet could stand. Poor little Piglet. Now Pooh understood why he got startled so easily.

"And the problem is compounded," Pooh went on, suddenly sounding very much like Owl, "by the fact that, as I've said, once CR goes to bed there's bugger-all to do here. Sometimes I feel like going and pushing over Owl's tree, like we did last time." Pooh's eyes briefly glowed with malicious excitement before becoming dull and bleary again.

Piglet blinched. If Pooh wanted to go off and start smashing things up he supposed he'd go too but right now he wasn't feeling in the mood. With a mixture of emotions, he remembered how, drunk and bored, they had earlier that year rampaged around the forest shouting and singing songs and waking everyone up before the ghastly denouement. Lord, how Mr Milne had roared at them. They had been very, very lucky, he had told them, that he was able to solve the problem with a story which had a rather milder build-up to do with a gale.

There had been a similar incident involving Eeyore's house, though they'd managed to convince everyone it had blown down in a snowstorm. Then Pooh had thrown that pole into the river, blocked up Rabbit's door and wrecked one of Mr M's precious bee-hives; worse still, Rabbit and Pooh and Piglet had tried to kill Tigger just after he'd arrived: the whole thing had backfired horribly and Rabbit had nearly died of exposure.

The three of them had also hatched a plan to kidnap Roo – another fiasco – which had culminated in Piglet's erotic episode with Kanga. And then there was that awful time they'd pulled Eeyore's tail off; the mad day they'd dug the huge hole in the path into which a drunk Pooh himself had later fallen and half killed himself – the charge sheet ran on and on.

Recently, Piglet had felt these random destructive feelings more and more strongly. As Pooh had pointed out, they had all been dragged off the scrap heap and it was surely to the scrap heap that they'd one day return. What did it matter what they did in-between? In a strange way, it almost felt better to have Mr Milne roar at them every so often rather than ignore them, as he normally did.

Piglet now wondered if Mr M had written his stories to cover up these acts of vandalism, abduction and assault. Or perhaps he allowed them to continue just to give him some inspiration? He supposed Mr Milne enjoyed having power over them. They also must have made him money, so enabling his son to enjoy the India-rubber balls, hoops, pencil boxes and bright blue braces of which he seemed to have an inexhaustible supply.

Piglet could just up and leave, of course, but the world was a frightening place, full of people like Trespassers William and Mr Sanders. It was easier to stay where they were, while it lasted, and spend as much time as possible getting pissed and kicking things over. That was just the way everything seemed to be. No escape plan had been provided and nothing about the way they'd been treated suggested they ought to consider creating one for themselves.

Pooh put the glass down. "God, this gin in disgusting. Tomorrow I'm going to get some Burgundy."

This was a another familiar Pooh riff. About a year before they'd stolen a bottle of Burgundy from Mr Milne's drawing room on one of the rare occasions they'd been allowed downstairs in the house. For Pooh, who'd drunk most of the bottle, repeating the experience had existed as a hopeless holy grail ever since.

Once they had struggled as far as the off-licence at Hartfield where Pooh had tried to buy two bottles of Gevery Chambertin on credit. Piglet, who wouldn't even have been able to see over the counter, had been left outside but had heard the contemptuous insults from the licensee. Ever since Pooh had, when in his cups, outlined various breaking-and-entering plans regarding the shop in which Piglet was to play a heroic role, being lowered in through a shattered skylight on 'a thin-ish piece of rope: or, if there isn't any, bring a thick-ish piece of string.' Pooh would guffaaw loudly at the memory of this rhyme.

Piglet was, up to a point, happy enough to play along with Pooh's fantasy. Their relationship depended on Pooh suggesting things and Piglet following on behind. However, the thought of raiding the off-licence filled him with real dread. So, whenever Pooh brought the subject up, he would quickly pass the bottle with the aim of ensuring that Pooh and sometimes himself were sufficiently pissed to prevent the suggestion from becoming a reality.

As a result of this and other circumstances, each of which served either to encourage or to justify the act of getting plastered every night, he and Pooh spent half the following days with Christopher Robin stumbling round in a bit of a blur. Although their animal instincts kicked in when CR appeared each morning, the physical toll of the night before took some time to wear off. Pooh was dopey and gruff until his so-called 'little something' at eleven o'clock. Mr

Milne was kind enough to imply this was half a pot of honey but Piglet knew it was this plus a slug of gin. By lunchtime, Pooh was normally OK, bumbling and good-natured for the next few hours. In summer, when there were normally evening adventures as well, Pooh generally needed another 'little something' at about half-past four. Piglet would often accompany him, sometimes gulping an egg-cup or two of honey vodka or, on more abstemious days, licking Pooh's plate clean of its sticky mixture of honey, condensed milk and haycorn gin.

Piglet's reactions to these dissipations often resulted, during the following day's unfeasible adventures, in a series of abject, blushing confusions and misjudgments which did nothing for his fragile self-esteem. Mr Milne was a strict 'story a day' man, 1,000 words without fail by tea time. Piglet was relieved most of these shallow farces never ended up in print. This combination of the humiliation and peril he risked during the day and heavy drinking he indulged in during the night, which carried with it the constant risk of being made to tramp across the Wood to commit an act of vandalism or burgle an off licence, was starting to play hell with his nerves.

Then Piglet realised something else. Most of Mr Milne's stories which *had* ended up in print were based on his and Pooh's worst drunken debacles. Perhaps they had more power than he thought in the situation? Although he couldn't begin to see how he might use this, the insight had given him a new perspective on life. Maybe he *was* worth something after all, if only as an inadvertent muse for Mr Milne's writing. This was hardly the basis of a career: but nor was racketing around as Pooh's side-kick in the only world they had ever really known but which they were fast outgrowing. There *had* to be something else but for the life of him Piglet couldn't work out what it was nor how he might attain it.

* * *

"Come *on*!" Christopher Robin shouted, "we're going to see Kanga and *Roo*!"

Pooh was lagging behind. He turned to Piglet. "Frankly, I can't face Kanga and Roo right now," he admitted, slipping alarmingly out of his conventional daytime character.

Piglet stood in the middle of the path. He looked at his little God dancing through the trees ahead of them in his freshly ironed blue knickerbockers, of the kind that Piglet would never own, the way things were. He looked at Pooh, fuzzled and frazzled and cross and seeming, he realised for the first time, to be slightly mad.

"Let's nip back to my place and have a quick snifter," Pooh said. "we can catch up with him later. Pretend we've fallen down a well or something. Milne will think of an explanation."

He gave a sarcastic snort which, at night, Piglet could relate to but which, in the middle of the Wood and with Christopher Robin only fifty feet away, slightly repulsed him. Pooh winked artlessly. "He probably needs us more than we need him."

The co-incidence of Pooh's thoughts and his own made Piglet feel thoroughly uncomfortable, torn in three different directions and with no moral compass to guide him towards or away from any of them.

He watched Christopher Robin jigging away along the path, still calling but now almost lost between the trees. Sooner or later, he would leave them, Piglet suddenly realised. At Galleon's Lap or wherever else there would be a moment when this time would end, when he would slip into another world that left no place for them. Already he could feel the strings that bound them starting to fray. But was today the day? He blinked a couple of times.

Christopher Robin had vanished. Pooh was still there, blinking as well, perhaps deep down as confused as Piglet was. But at least he, like Christopher Robin, had a plan.

"Let's have a drink," Pooh repeated. Expecting that Piglet would follow, he turned and stumped off down the left-hand path. "Then," Pooh added over his shoulder, "I think it'll be high time to get that Burgundy. Today's the day..."

Piglet stood stock still in the centre of the little junction of paths. Both Christopher Robin and Pooh had now vanished. For the first time in what felt like ages he was alone. The rain had stopped. The clouds were parting and few shafts of sunshine slanted through the trees. The world, or what little he knew of it, was spread out before him. He could choose what to do. Piglet almost swooned – it didn't take much – at the thought. He could choose!

"Come *on*!" he heard Christopher Robin's voice call from ahead of him.

"Where the *hell* are you?" he heard Pooh's voice growl from the left a few moments later.

To the right was another path that led to the Pooh-sticks bridge and, beyond that, to the world beyond the Wood.

Still Piglet didn't move. He only had a few seconds to decide. What *was* he going to do?

The Old Man and the Tree

I don't think Ernest Hemingway ever visited East Garston or set one of his stories there. If he did, there seems to be no record of it. It doesn't seem likely at all. But I suppose he might have done...

IT RAINED HARD that spring. Most mornings the old man sat and watched the men going to work in the fields. If it was raining they would mostly be wearing hats but whether it was raining or not they would all have thick boots. You had to have thick boots working in the fields. Every so often they would stop to knock some of the mud off their boots but pretty soon they'd have to stop and do it all over again. Time was when the old man would have been up there with them working in the fields but he didn't go up to the fields any more because of the accident. If it hadn't been for that damned accident he'd probably be up there working now.

After a while the men were just specks in the distance and the old man would get tired of watching them. He could imagine what they were doing well enough, anyway. Then he would get up and slowly walk to the *Bar Reina*. It would take him a long time because the wound from the accident still gave him trouble. So he would walk slowly, stopping every so often and then going on again.

Sometimes he would pass the tree. Whether he passed the tree or not depended on what route he took. If he took the route that didn't go past the tree he wouldn't see it but sometimes he forgot and sometimes he just wanted to see the damned tree even though it had been a part of the accident. If it was one of those days he would stop and look at the tree as if it was a wild creature. Then he would carry on to the bar, thinking about the tree.

There was a morning when he was in the bar drinking *cerveza* and nibbling at some *patatas crispas*. That was the morning the young man came in. As soon as the old man noticed the young man he turned his face away from him as if he didn't want to be seen. For a long while the young man stood at the bar talking to Federico and drinking *caffé instanto*. Then the young man turned round and came over to the table.

"Hello, old one," the young man said. "You are still here, then."

"Yes," the old man said, "I am still here."

"Some said you had gone away to Lambournos or Sheffordo Grande."

"No," the old man said, "I have not gone away."

"Let me buy you an *alcopopos*, old one," the man said.

"I do not drink the *alcopopos* any more," the old man said. "I drink the *cerveza* and the *Oporto* and the *Jerez* and the *Malibu-coca-cola*, but I do not drink the *alcopopos* any more. Not since the accident have I drunk the *alcopopos*."

"Of course." The young man looked down at the ground. "Tell me about the accident."

The old man just looked out of the window at the fields where the men were working, although he couldn't see them now. They had probably gone over the hill by this time, he figured. Sometimes when people walk for a long time they get so far away that you can't see them any more. That was the way it was with these men.

"It was a long time ago, the accident," the old man said at last.

"Two weeks is a long time ago?" the young asked.

"Every day has been a long day since then. You are young. What do you know about time?" The old man spat on the floor.

They both fell silent and watched Federico putting menus on the tables. Federico was the owner of the *Reina*. His way of putting menus on the tables was to go from table to table, putting one menu on each. Once he had put one menu down he would go right on to the next table and put another menu down there, too. He didn't come near the table where the two men were talking because he knew that since the accident the old man didn't feel so hot about eating food or doing anything much except drinking the *cerveza* and watching the men going to work in the fields.

"So," the young man said, "it was a long time ago." He said this as if it didn't matter to him whether it was a long time ago or not.

"Yes," the old man said. "It was a long time ago. And it was all because of the *alcopopos*. I must tell you first that I do not drink the *alcopopos* any more," the old man said. "So, even if you were to buy me one I could not drink it, not even if it was poured into a glass of *cerveza*."

The young man got up and walked up to the bar. He had to pass several of the tables where the menus had been laid out but he didn't pay them any mind. He just walked up to the bar and spoke quietly to Federico. The next thing he was back at the table with a large glass of the *cerveza*. This he placed in front of the old man. It was a reddish kind of *cerveza*. It was like the kind they used to make by grinding the barley hard in the *presso* and leaving it to roast in the *kilnos* for a very long time but this *cerveza* hadn't been made that way.

"Drink your *cerveza*, old one, and tell me about the accident. Is it because of the accident that you do not work in the fields any more?"

"You are right," the old man said. "It is because of the accident." He took a draught of the *cerveza* so that when he put the glass down there were some droplets on his lip. Then he wiped his mouth and the droplets were gone. "Sometimes I do not want to talk about the accident," he said. "Sometimes I do not want to think about why I am not working in the fields any more."

"Tell me," the young man said.

"Very well. I will tell you. A long time ago I was in this bar. It was late at night and I was drinking *alcopopos*. I was drinking *alcopopos* like a man drinks them." He smacked his fist on the table. The young man nodded. The old man took another sip of of his drink. Then he put it down. "Some nights they sell *alcopopos* cheap."

The young man nodded. He knew that some nights they sold the *alcopopos* cheap, too. Some nights it was expensive but on other nights they might have a *promocion* and the *alcopopos* would be cheap and sometimes other things as well. That was the way it was.

"I was drinking *alcopopos* late into the night, even though the next day I knew I would have to get up early and work in the fields. When the time came I left the bar and started to walk home. I had not gone a hundred paces when I found that I had walked into a tree." He pointed out of the window. The young man looked too. "I was on my back. Then I knew I had had an accident. My ankle had twisted and I could not walk. I had to crawl back to the bar, like a dog. Ever since then I have not gone to work in the fields."

"But soon you will be well again, old one. A week – perhaps two, and you will be well again. Then you will be able to work in the fields again, with the men."

"Perhaps," said the old man.

This was the story the old man told that morning, drinking his *cerveza*. I do not know whether he got better and went to work in the fields with the men or not because a few days later I went away from the village for good and never saw any of them again.

King Richard IV (Part One)

I don't know if Shakespeare was familiar with Hungerford or anywhere in West Berkshire, nor if he was interested in maps or the fate of England's traditional counties. But I suppose he might have been...

Act 1, Scene 1
The Earl of Berkshire's castle in Hungerford

Enter King Richard IV and the Earl of Berkshire

KING RICHARD IV The sceptered land is set about with grief
    Since traitorous Westmoreland hath raised his arms
    Against our royal person in the north
    And Sussex, from the south, we have but learned,
    Has joined him in this venture. Nay, say not
    'tis just against myself: for all our land,
    Our body politic, our common weal
    And all we hold most dear is threatened thus.
BERKSHIRE Between the upper and the lower thrusts
    Of thankless dogs we stand to be enmeshed.
KING RICHARD IV If metaphors or fine words must there be,
    My Lord of Berkshire, pray leave them to me.
    But I have something to unseat them yet;
    Behold a map I have this day received –
    Mark how it shows the contours of our realm
    The hills and towns, the roads that link them, so.
    Now I at last can plan a full defence
    Of our encircled throne.

BERKSHIRE It is all truly wonderous to the eye;
     The ochre dark, the lapis lazuli
     And other colours: reds and golds and browns
     The cursive script, the details of the towns;
     A fair reflection of our gracious land
     This lovely thing was made – by whose fair hand?
KING RICHARD IV Master Saxton, Christopher, hath wrought it
     Humble printed it, and I have bought it.
BERKSHIRE Bought it from where, my Lord?
KING RICHARD IV From a merchant in your town of Hungerford
     Who deals in objects which, though striking new to me,
     Have yet the flavour of antiquity.
BERKSHIRE There are many such, and will be many more.
     But hark – there's someone knocking at the door.
KING RICHARD IV Well, go and let them in, then.
BERKSHIRE My Lord, it shall be done *(exit)*
KING RICHARD IV Being alone, I know I should now be
     Addressing you in a soliloquy.
     Yet though this moment soon will pass away,
     I cannot think of anything to say.

Enter the Earls of Kintbury and Lambourn

KING RICHARD IV Cousin Kintbury, glad I am to see you
     And fair Lambourn too – a double welcome to you both.
KINTBURY My liege, as soon as tidings reached us
     In our several halls, we vaulted
     Straightway on our steeds and sped
     Towards your majesty. Though Hecuba herself
     Were snapping at our heels, we were swifter yet:
     If all the sprites of Hades...
KING RICHARD IV Yes, yes, you came as quickly as you could

Let that suffice for now, the time is brief:
Too short for musings on your gallant haste
How fast you rode, how quickly you did sup –
'til I decide to bring the matter up.

LAMBOURN   Your majesty commands, so we obey
No more shall e'er be said about the way
In which we hastened, breathless to be here...

KING RICHARD IV   Enough already – have I not been clear?
My lords, we are at war within. Sussex
And Westmoreland in dreadful harness
Seek to despoil our throne. I swear
I shall not rest til I have carved
Their counties into pieces. I shall wreak
A vengeance on the very grass beneath their feet
I'll spoil it, raze it, burn out all the sap:
In short, my friends, I'll wipe them from the map.

KINTBURY   A map, my liege? Pray tell me, what's a map?

KING RICHARD IV   Where have you been? I'faith, what are you like?
This here's a map. This paper landscape
Now stands between ourselves and utter ruin.
The man who holds a map knows where he stands
And holds the kingdom firmly in his hands.

KINTBURY   Oh, yes.

KING RICHARD IV   Unmetric!

KINTBURY   Yes, yes – yes, oh yes.
I get it now; I think so; more or less.

KING RICHARD IV   We tarry overlong – you must away
And summon forth, before the close of day
My lords of Inkpen, Garston, Ham and Combe
Gentle Chaddleworth, and Thatcham too
To meet us three days hence, in full array
And thence to battle – come, whyfore delay?

LAMBOURN We're clear, my lord, about the when and who;
    The where still lacks: we need a rendez-vous.
KING RICHARD IV Good point; well said; your wits are yet alive
    In these uncertain times. Pray give me five.
LAMBOURN We await your pleasure. *(exeunt)*

Enter The Queen

QUEEN My lord, must you go to war so soon?
KING RICHARD IV My lady, that I must. The realm is sore divided
    Wild Sussex and Westmoreland have ventured forth
    A challenge to our kingly state, which we
    Are forced to meet head on, and not refuse...
QUEEN I know all that – I heard it on the news.
    I only ask because I need to know
    If Sussex sups on Friday with us?
KING RICHARD IV No: all things considered, probably best not.
QUEEN I'll tell the cook, then, now. Oh, nice map. What
    Projection is it? Bonne? Gall-Peters? Or
    Cassini? No – it's Transverse Mercator!
KING RICHARD IV This is all Greek to me. Of more import
    You'll see it shows the organs of our realm.
    Westmoreland's so huge, while Rutland's not
    With Saxton's map, I know my real foe.
QUEEN Size isn't everything, my gracious lord, you know. *(exit)*
KING RICHARD IV What was all that about? No matter.
    Where was I? Ah yes, this fair map
    Shows me what is now my sacred realm;
    But, in times to come, men might yet seek
    An understanding of my brutal age.
    Perchance – but here my fancy leads me on –
    They might make gifts of just such works of war

Elegantly framed and printed for
Nostalgic gifts or genealogy
Sold via the web (whatever that might be).
The present time will thus forever last
If men will make a present of the past.

Enter Kintbury and Lambourn

KINTBURY My lord, the time chafes at our wings.
KING RICHARD IV I am decided: we shall meet in three
    days time – where rhymes? Ah yes, at Newbury.
    But bid them all be there while it's still light:
    The traffic's terrible on Friday night.
LAMBOURN All shall be done, my lord. *(exeunt)*
KING RICHARD IV Alone again. I'm now quite in the swing
    Of holding forth on every little thing
    That falls into my mind: so I'll unbend
    A tale to you – 'twas told me by a friend
    And what is more, he swears that it be true.
    It seems, one day a Scotsman and a Jew
    Went to an inn, and...

Enter Rutland

KING RICHARD IV *(aside)* Always the one to spoil my jests.
    Greetings, little Rutland; hast thou come
    To see that civil war will not be done
    Without the vassals that you can deploy
    What are they – three men and a boy?
    I jesteth; or perhaps I mean I jest;
    Your men will all be welcomed with the rest.
    We meet at Newbury – farewell. *(exit)*

RUTLAND Farewell my king. My king, indeed farewell.
    Little Rutland; how the phrase doth grate
    Upon the dignity of my estate.
    Sussex, Westmoreland, other lords beside
    Have counties of a decent sort of size;
    But mine is not: my reputation's wrecked
    By sour contempt, instead of just respect.
    But listen close: Westmoreland and Sussex
    I have entwined in this endeavour. Others too:
    Even the queen – my modesty recoils
    To tell of how I've used her in this broil.
    My hand in all of this is full unseen.
    Who would suspect that Little Rutland could
    Unleash such mayhem? From the sparks
    Of this great fire I'll forge a shield
    To keep my patrimony whole.

Enter King Richard IV

KING RICHARD IV Still here, small Rutland?
RUTLAND I am counting my vassals, sire.
KING RICHARD IV Count them well – miss not even two
    But being half your whole, 'tis hard to do. *(exit)*
RUTLAND See what I mean? I know he has a map
    That chafes me more than anything. It shows
    My Rutland small as charity, as though
    'twere hardly there at all. I swear I'll show
    Those other lords how destiny will flow.
    Sussex, Berkshire, other counties too
    Will one day cease to be, or be in two.
    A curse on counties of a generous size!
    Mark me well – yes, Rutland will survive. *(exit)*

Fear and Loathing in East Garston

I don't think Hunter S. Thompson ever visited West Berkshire or set one of his stories there. If he did, there seems to be no record of it. It doesn't seem likely at all. But I suppose he might have done…

WE WERE SOMEWHERE around Boxford on the edge of the downs when the drugs began to take hold. I remember saying something like "I feel a bit lightheaded; maybe you should drive…" and suddenly there was a terrible neighing all around and the road was full of what looked like horses swooping and screeching all around the car, which was going at about twenty-nine miles an hour with the windows down towards East Garston. And a voice was screaming "What *are* those animals?"

Then it was quiet again. "What were you shouting about?" my attorney muttered.

"Never mind," I said. "It's your turn to drive."

"We've only got another six miles. What's the *matter* with you?"

I changed down and hauled the Vauxhall round a corner. No point mentioning those horses, I thought. The poor idiot will see them soon enough.

Six miles to go. They would be tough miles. Very soon we would both be completely twisted. There was no going back and no time to rest. We were fastbacking it from Reading to cover Harriet's gig for the *Chronicle*. Check-in at the Queen's Arms was at seven and the gig kicked off at nine. It was now six so we had absolutely no margin for error. The editor had fronted us fifty notes and we had spent the afternoon in Theale rounding up a collection of medication. We probably wouldn't end up needing most of this stuff but when two hypochondriacs get locked into a serious medicine collection the tendency is to push it as far as you can.

In the car we had fifty anti-histamine, a box of Panadol, four dozen Strepsils, a litre of Benelin, two jars of Rennies, a pack of Pro-Plus, several tubs of Alka-Selzer a quart of Pepto Bismol and ten packets of Fishermen's Friends. In the boot was a case of Diet Coke, a bottle of Fanta, two litres of Perrier and – in case things really slipped anchor – a half-bottle of Beaujolais and a pack of Resolve.

The green downs shimmered in the sunlight. I was concentrating on holding the Vectra at exactly thirty and nearly missed the pub. I pulled into the car park. It was almost empty. Too empty, perhaps. I glanced around and forced another handful of Rennies into my mouth to head off the worst of the paranoia. Paranoia is the one to miss. It's the mocking face on the dashboard clock, the mirthless grin in the rear-view, the repeating question throbbing up through the leatherette upholstery, asking: 'have I got the wrong day?'

My attorney was out of the car like a mad bat almost before I'd stopped. He'd always had a weak bladder and the coffee at Chieveley Services was getting to him. I took a moment to do some breathing exercises and get my hair straightened out before following him into the pub. Registration was the next hurdle and there was no way of telling if we'd clear it. Already I could sense the rape pollen about to trigger a hay-fever attack, could feel the hang-nail on my thumb start to throb at the thought of signing a guest-book. It seemed very unlikely we'd even get as far as the bar in our condition – that was, if my attorney hadn't already been barred for knocking down the door of the gent's in some hideous caffeine-fuelled rage.

It seemed he'd done his business without any obvious damage and was at the reception counter, babbling at a blonde woman about sinusitis and proprietary vapour rubs. I would have to take over if the situation wasn't to get completely out of hand, like that time in Twyford. "Twin room, booked for the *Chronicle*," I said, but the words came out wrong, like the buzzing of a wasp, or a man speaking underwater. I swallowed my lozenge, blew my nose a couple of times and tried again.

She said she'd show us the room. It all seemed relaxed enough, but you never could tell. I walked about six paces behind in case she wanted to make small-talk. Normal people aren't wise to sociopaths like us, they take all the mumbling and fumbling the wrong way. I sidled up to my attorney and hissed, "don't say anything about those horses," but he his eyes were completely glazed and I don't think he heard me. I had to remember to tell him to take his contacts and ear plugs out.

When we got to the room my attorney at once shot off into the bathroom to avoid having to decide whether to tip her. I froze. The woman talked of this and that but her words made no sense to me. Then, suddenly, she had gone. From the bathroom came the sound of my attorney trying to flush the toilet. We were a mess and no mistake, wired to the teeth on preventative medication and still hours away from the gig. This was the Big One, my first solo review commission. It was just round the corner and I wasn't sure if I could make it all the way. There was only one thing to do.

"I'm going to have kip," I said. "That drive has ripped me up."

"Good idea," he said. Two minutes later the Eezy-Snooze kicked in and we were asleep.

* * *

It was nearly nine and we were in the bar, leaning into large orange and sodas and trying to cut the worst effects of the Night Nurse we'd wolfed down in the room by taking handfuls of Rennies and Pro-Plus. The band were setting up in the far corner, but I didn't feel straight enough to go and chat. The floor seemed uneven – in fact it was moving in lurid waves like a nightmare pink and green sea. The faces of the people standing at the far end of the bar were the same colours…then everything changed to purple and yellow. I dug my nails into the edge of the bar counter, trying to get a grip on myself. I thought about warning my attorney but then remembered he was colour-blind. There were times when it was an advantage. He hadn't seen those horses, either.

"Look," he said, "that guy over there – it's Bruno Brookes, isn't it? You know, the ex-DJ?"

I gripped his arm. "You're going to have to get yourself under control. I'm seeing horrible things too, you know. Just keep cool."

For some reason we had started to shout. My attorney was half deaf anyway and I'd had both ears syringed two days before as a precautionary measure and hadn't yet adjusted to the new acoustics in my head. Later on, when the music kicked in, we'd be roaring like apes but right now it was probably as well not to crank it up too high. People were starting to stare. I slid a couple of Rennies across the counter. "Take these," I muttered, "they'll kill the reflux."

"Are you trying to poison me?" he yelled. "I've already had six today! I'm on the max!"

I shrugged. I like to have my attorney along in case anything I cover – flower shows, weddings and so on – needs an immediate legal opinion for defamation or libel. It was also mandatory to have someone to talk to; dealing with strangers was a step too far for me.

Yet, to my alarm, my attorney was now trying to talk to the blonde woman who had earlier checked us in. One false move could be fatal. I grabbed his shoulder and spun him round. It turned out he was trying to order more orange and sodas.

"Tell her to keep them coming," I hissed, "every fifteen minutes on the nail. That way we don't have to talk and blow our cover. We're too wired for chit-chat."

The woman came back with the change. "So, you're here to see the gig? They're just about to start. Haven't I seen you around – up at the stables perhaps?"

I froze. Horses again. Or was this some code the straights used to weed out cruisers who were running on heavy fuel? Suddenly there was a loud guitar chord behind me. My reason snapped.

"We saw horses today on the road," I roared. "Loads of them. About four!"

"Oh, yes," she said, "I thought I recognised you." Her face became sterner. "You gave them a fright. One of you was shouting. My horse nearly threw me."

This was it – we'd been clocked while indulging in bad craziness on a public highway. The next stage would be the cops: and then questions, questions, questions. If there was thing I hated it was questions from cops. Or anyone else.

I grabbed my attorney and pulled him off the stool. Our drinks smashed on the floor, the grey stone floor: not a purple sea at all, now the strobe light had been turned off.

"We're out of here!" I yelled. Then I was stumbling across the car park in a hunched run, my attorney floundering in my wake. We dashed into the room and grabbed our stash of drugs, threw clothes into bags. Then it was out to the car. I fumbled for keys and forced my attorney into the passenger seat.

"I wanna go back," he wailed.

"Get real," I snarled as I carefully executed a six-point turn. "They're onto us. Our only hope is that they didn't clock the plates. Otherwise we're dead meat. Now – give me a Strepsil."

We turned onto the road, heading for Lambourn. No one seemed to be watching us leave but that didn't mean anything. Just because they're not watching you leave it doesn't mean they're not watching you. We passed through Eastbury in a blur – we must have been doing at least thirty-five. With only two pints of soda water inside me dehydration was still a problem but I'd just have to ride it out.

"What about the review?" my attorney asked.

"How about 'at The *Queen's Arms* on Saturday night, Harriet's five-piece bluegrass combo entertained a large gathering with a well-appreciated blend of original songs and old favourites. A good time was had by all.' Then we use the photo she sent of some other show. See – easy." I felt myself starting to relax. Our next gig was a jumble sale in Shefford next Sunday so we had eight days to get straightened out for that.

Carefully, I changed down gear. We were driving due west into the last glows of a blood-red sunset. All around us the downs were fading into shadow.

Professor Sebastian Bryson-Bragg Explains the Third Mood

HI THERE PEEPS – I'm the Robert Robinson Professor of Neological Linguistics at the University of Stoke Poges. Quite a mouthful! But you can call me Prof BB which is what my students do (or some of them!) I like to think I'm a pretty approachable kind of guy and that I tell things how they are with a smile on my face – which has got to be a good thing, right? Someone told me that I was the Tony Blair of neological linguistics and you don't get any higher praise than that in my book (and I've written a few)!

You've probably noticed that I like to use exclamation marks (!) Not quite the image of a stuffy professor of words! Hey, that's just showing how enthusiastic I am! I'm so happy that God has given me this gift of communication. If that needs extra punctuation now and then to really sock it home, so be it! If you want to learn you've got to make it fun :-)

Right guys – let's get seriouso. What's this third mood, then? Nothing to do with tri-polar disorder! I'm talking verbs. We know about the active and the passive, don't we? 'I ate' and 'I have been eaten'? Well, there's a third, too: the manipulative. This is a recent addition so don't go looking for it in the books (except mine, natch)! It first appeared in the early 1980s and is generally found in only two areas of life: marketing and politics. Example time!

Imagine you're reading an advertisement for a financial product which starts with the sentence: *'You want the best for your family.'* If you parsed this, you might say 'easy – present indicative.' You'd be wrong – wrong, wrong, *wrong*! In this context, it's what we language boffs call the 'continuous manipulative'.

So, what's that, Prof BB?

To explain, we need to wind back one moment, chaps and chapesses. Were you to have seen the sentence in isolation, your first guess would have been right. What makes it manipulative is what happens *afterwards*. What happens *afterwards* is a series of statements that, though individually dubious, becomes reasonable following acceptance of the first remark.

We'd all agree with wanting what's best for our family, wouldn't we? Course we would! Once this has been established, it becomes progressively harder to disagree with what is said afterwards, as long as it appears to be connected to the first point – hence the 'manipulative'. This illusion of agreement continues for as long as you carry on reading – hence the 'continuous'. Put the two words together and what've you got? That's it – 'continuous manipulative'.

The easiest way to get people to feel this connection is to start as many of the subsequent sentences with a word or phrase like 'so', 'therefore', 'obviously' or 'in order that'. Time for another example!

'You want the best for your family. Therefore you will want to become as rich as possible. In order for this to happen, you should seriously consider robbing a bank.'

See what I mean? As long as you start with something that no one will disagree with, the whole proposition appears eminently reasonable. A phrase such as 'you should seriously consider' adds some volts to the continuous manipulativeness of the initial verb: it challenges the reader seriously to consider something and then, just at the point when his or her brain has started trying to do so, pops up with the answer – rob a bank! With the right typeface and a compelling illustration at the top, by the end of the first paragraph a lot of readers will think that the whole thing had been their own idea. Job done!

So much for marketing. Now we turn to politics, where the use of the third mood is even more dramatic. I'd like at this point to ask our former Prime Minister to step forward. Hi Theresa! She, more than anyone else I'm aware of, is a compulsive user of the classic continuous-manipulative verb 'to be clear.'

Like *falloir* in French (sorry, Brexiteers!) 'to be clear' is a defective verb. *Falloir* only exists in the third person singular: 'to be clear', in the third mood, only exists in the first person singular and the first person plural. Ding-dong! Example time again!

'*I want to be clear...*' (invariably used in answer to a question.) This conveys, in only five words, a whole raft of implications: (1) that the question was muddled or obscure, even though the reality was that it was merely unwelcome; (2) that all previous attempts by the politician so far in the interview to be clear have been thwarted by the interviewer; (3) that the politician is trying to lay down the law to some rebellious faction in their party; (4) that something important is about to be said which will bring all the confused wrangling we've been listening to so far into sharp focus. We all want things to be clear, yes? Clarity is good, right? Course it is! Well, the implication is, here comes some clarity – so listen up!

If the politician adds 'very' or 'quite', as in '*I want to be very clear...*' that conveys all the above meanings plus (5) hey journos – 280-character soundbite coming up!

As with the marketing example, once you accept the premise that the admirable goal of clarity is what's being aimed at, more or less anything that's said afterwards will be accepted (and, if 'quite' or 'very' is used, also written down and quoted in a headline).

So, that's the singular form. The plural form, which we linguos call the 'continuous inclusive manipulative' (hea-vy term, sorry guys!) is, in the right hands, one of the most powerful weapons in a politician's arsenal. Are you ready-steady-go?

'*Let us be quite clear...*' You see what I mean? Wow – packs a punch, doesn't it? Nanny may have just smacked your wrists but now she's putting her arm around you and is inviting you, in the midst of your distress and confusion, to share her world, in which everything is clear and simple and easy just as long as you do what you're told. All you have to do is nod and agree to eat your sprouts! At this point you're whimpering so loudly that you can't even hear what she's saying: but it no longer matters. Nanny's in charge so everything's going to be hunky dory.

So, there we have it – Prof BB's lightning tour of one of the most unrecognised grammatical forms of our time – the third mood. There might even be fourth mood – hey, that's an exciting thought, isn't it? Sort of like a fourth dimension! Groovy! Who needs Brian Cox when you've got a neological linguist on your team?

Laters!

The Case of the Missing Teaspoons

A FEW MONTHS ago we had a dozen. Then it went down to eight. A couple of weeks back I could only find three. Last week, there was just the one.

Sorry – in my excitement I've left out an important detail. I'm talking about teaspoons. Our teaspoons have been disappearing. Time was there was barely enough room in the cutlery drawer for them. Not now.

Other things have been vanishing as well. The mugs used to fill two shelves of the cupboard: now they barely occupy one. Double sheets and tea towels too. All these things we used to have, if not an embarrassment of, then at least a comfortable supply. Now we're almost down to sleeping on bare mattresses, drying up with paper towels and drinking tea and coffee out of vases or egg cups.

In such cases, the wise man summons expert advice. I made some calls and soon had four appointments. To make them feel at home, I slipped out to buy *sirop de menthe*, a packet of Lapsang, a seven-per-cent solution of cocaine and a bottle of Bourbon, none of these being things we normally keep in the house.

Holmes was the first, Watson following with a notebook, like some North Korean flunkey ready for on-the-spot guidance. Holmes looked awful but perked up after a shot of the seven-per-cent. While the great detective was dealing with this in the bathroom, Watson and I chatted about his time in Afghanistan in the 1880s. He was saddened though not surprised when I said that, 140-odd years later, the war there was still going on.

I told Holmes my story. He listened with great attentiveness, his hands pressed together, the tips of his fingers resting against his lower lip. When I had finished he sat back and closed his eyes.

"A most singular narrative," he said at last, "and one that presents several features of interest. You first noticed these disappearances about three months ago?"

"Yes."

"Did anything else happen about that time?"

I thought back to mid-July. "One of our cats disappeared."

"And hasn't returned." I was about to ask how he knew but he anticipated me. "There's only one feeding bowl."

"Might these things be connected, Holmes?" Watson asked in that dim and dogged way he has.

"I cannot say. It is a capital error to formulate a hypothesis on insufficient data." He was silent for a moment, lightly drumming his fingers on the table. Then he stood up. "I would like to examine the kitchen, as that appears to be the principal scene of the crime. The sheets we shall leave to one side for the present."

He then subjected the room to a minute scrutiny, much of which was conducted on his hands and knees. He took samples from the dust, fluff, pieces of onion skin, stray cat biscuits and the other things which are normally found on our kitchen floor. He looked in the drawers, under the sink and on top of the cupboards. It was impossible not to smile.

"You find my survey amusing," he said, though not unkindly, when he had finished. "It is rare these fail to reveal features which have a bearing on the case."

"Has it on this occasion?" I asked.

"There are four things of cardinal importance and nine others which may prove to be so. As you may know from the sensationalist accounts my dear friend Dr Watson has fashioned, I keep my own counsel until I am certain the quarry is in sight."

"But surely..." Watson gasped, his pen poised.

Holmes closed his eyes, as if with boredom. "Beyond the obvious facts that the person who prepares most of the vegetables is left-handed, that the household has changed its brand of dishwasher powder twice in the last month, that chickens are kept here but have not recently been laying, that a guitar has been re-strung and that the fridge has a tendency to leak, no."

"But Holmes!" Watson expostulated. (He expostulates at least once in each case: I was glad he was running true to form.) "How could you possibly..."

"He's quite right," I said.

Holmes almost purred. "The angle of the marks on the chopping board are suggestive and became conclusive when I examined the blade of the paring knife. There are rings where glasses and mugs are placed in the cupboard which reveal three different types of powder. The trained eye can distinguish at least thirty-five different brands. Perhaps you have read my monograph on the subject?"

I confessed that I had not.

"No matter. The evidence suggests you ran out of your preferred type, substituted it for something else which was unsatisfactory and then moved to a third which proved even more so." He cocked his eye at me. I nodded. "For that machine, given you consume a lot of rice, I advise Sainsbury's Powerball-plus." I thanked him for the suggestion. He sat back, now warming to his task. "The bowl on the window ledge is where you keep eggs. There is plentiful evidence in the form of straw and small feathers to suggest this has been used for storing these fresh from the fowls. However, the ones currently there are shop-bought. The inference then becomes obvious. As for the guitar, there is the ball-end of a top E by the dustbin – probably a nine-gauge Ernie Ball – and a small cross-section of a thicker string, probably an A, on the floor by the oven. Top Es break sometimes, As rarely: for both to break at the same time is inadmissible. *Ergo*, all the strings were changed. The sometimes-leaking fridge reveals itself by the slight discolouration on the linoleum."

"But the rice, Holmes!" Watson was expostulating again. "How did you know *that*?"

"There's a big bag of it in the cupboard."

I was becoming bored by what was starting to look like showing off. We were also getting off the point. "What about the spoons?"

"This will receive my fullest attention," Holmes said curtly and got to his feet. "There are several promising lines of enquiry. I hope to have more definite news before the weekend." He gave a final glance round the room. "I note that you currently don't have any domestic servants."

"You could lose the 'currently'. We've never had any."

"I see," Holmes said after the briefest of pauses and swept out, Watson wallowing in his wake.

Poirot was up next. Remembering his obsession for neatness and order, things in short supply here, I feared that he would refuse to set foot in the place. His good manners prevailed, however, and a glass of *sirop* put him slightly at his ease, if not to the extent that he could be persuaded to sit down. Instead he paced the kitchen in his patent-leather shoes while I told him the story.

"*Mille pardons*," he said at one point, holding up his hand. "So – we have twenty of your English feet this way and sixteen this. Most interesting...but please – conclude your most fascinating narrative, I implore you."

When I done so he stood still in the exact middle of the room, carefully stroking his moustache. "Most intriguing," he said. "I need to grasp the *psychology* of this crime. Some things still perplex me."

"I find the whole thing perplexing."

Poirot smiled. "But of course you do, *mon ami!*" he said. "That is what Hercule Poirot is for, to shed light in the darkness." He clapped his hands. "Now – first, I interview the members of your household."

"Penny's out and the boys are at school. That just leaves me."

"But the servants?"

"We have no servants."

"Indeed?" the dapper Belgian sleuth replied. He looked about him, much as Holmes had earlier done, then nodded. "I see. Well, I shall not derange you further. I shall now return home and apply the little grey cells to this problem of the tea spoons for a day or so. You may expect to hear from Hercule Poirot when the solution has been divined. The issue is, *sans doute*, a psychological one." With this enigmatic remark he took his leave.

I had only just got the tea made when Miss Marple arrived, pink, flustered and apologetic for being five minutes late. "My nephew, Raymond – the writer: *terribly* clever but he does make such *silly* mistakes sometimes, like the time he insisted GK Chesterton was French. He *would* take a short cut which was anything but, as they often are. In the long run one is better sticking to the main roads, despite the traffic. At least there are *signs*."

During all this I managed to divest her of her coat, manoeuvre her into a chair and provide a cup of tea. I recounted the problem.

"Oh, I *do* see," said when I'd finished. "It reminds me *so* much of when Mrs Crabbit in the village believed she'd lost a brooch – not valuable, but you know how people claim an affection for an object once it's gone missing whereas they never seemed to care for it when it was sitting on the dressing table – then a hat, and then a goldfish bowl. And her poor maid Ethel was in tears as she thought she was being accused of theft, which she was in a way, although she's the most honest girl: from the village, you see. I've known her all her life so you *know* these things but Mrs Crabbit didn't choose to see what was under her nose. Dear me. Then it turned out to be the *most* absurd misunderstanding, to do with the vicar's son who, on the other hand, was *not* to be trusted *one inch*."

She nodded a few times, lost in her memories. Beyond suggesting the tea-spoon question would prove to be a muddle in some way of my making, we seemed no further advanced. I coughed lightly.

"I'm sorry – a silly old woman talking about people you don't know and all the time you need to discover what has happened to your spoons. Now – how long have your servants been with you?"

"We have no servants," I said for the third time that day.

While the other two had merely been surprised, Miss Marple seemed genuinely upset. "Oh dear. That is to say, I know that people now have *very* different ideas about how a house should be run. I suppose you cook your own food?"

"We do, and will continue to do so until all the cutlery and the crockery has vanished," I said dryly, making another attempt to drag the conversation back to the matter in hand.

"How very modern." She looked at me narrowly. "My point *really* was that...well, it's not a nice thing to say – but, if it's just you and your family living here then it does rather *narrow it down*, doesn't it? I know anyone could have stolen them but it's the fact they've been disappearing gradually that is so very interesting. Why risk returning when you could take what you wanted in one go? And what a fascinating assortment of objects. What were they? Tea spoons, sheets, mugs – *cups* of course, in my day – tea towels...oh, of *course*! I see now what has been happening..."

There was a melodious toot of a car horn from outside. Miss Marple stood up.

"That's Raymond – he does so *hate* to be kept waiting. This has been terribly interesting. I'll be staying in the area for a few days so I shall certainly return. I just need to think about...tell me, do you have cats?"

"Yes. Two until recently. Now just the one. We're about to get two more."

"How very interesting." The horn tooted again. Before I had the chance to ask about her insight into the pattern of the missing objects she was off down the garden path and giving me a delicate wave, like the Queen Mother after opening a supermarket.

Marlowe was an hour late. He had a bruise on his face, which I didn't ask about, and a half-smoked cigarette in his mouth which he eventually doused in the remains of Miss Marple's cup of Lapsang. I uncorked the Bourbon and gave him a large shot. He drank it off and poured another while I described the problem.

"You called the law?"

"No."

"Any reason why not?"

"I didn't think they'd be interested."

"Maybe not. If it's not a strangled blonde in a Chinatown flophouse with a press angle the big boys figure it's not worth the candle. You'd end up with a sap like Nulty who'd get the whole thing so ballsed up he'd pinch his grandmother and have her on a rap before the DA's office could pull the shutters."

I agreed this wasn't at all the kind of outcome I was hoping for.

"They worth anything, these spoons? Jade handles, silver filigree, that sort of thing?"

"No."

"Sentimental value?"

"No. The point is..."

"From a dame? Dames buy presents sometimes, so I'm told."

"There's my wife, but..."

"I was thinking of another kind of dame, if you take my drift."

I took his drift. "Nothing like that."

"There normally is." He poured himself another slug of whisky and then, for no reason I could see, put his hat back on and at once took it off again. "There's usually a dame. I warn my clients but nothing seems to do any good." He lit another cigarette. "Trouble is, the dame often *is* the client. I should never have taken cases from dames, ju-ju men or one-legged conjurers from Cincinnati."

"No, quite. So..."

"OK, you want to get back to the spoons. That's jake with me.

Anyone tried to sell them back?"

"No."

"Uh-ha." He put his hat back on and stood up. "Problem with a case like this is knowing where to start. It's like playing blackjack in a Vegas funeral parlour with a pair of damp Mexican riding gloves strapped to your trousers." He knocked back the rest of his whisky and refilled his glass. After some further wisecracks he'd finished the bottle. Then he got into his car and drove off, having promised to return with news in a couple of days.

I started washing up. The last tea spoon had disappeared. There were no tea towels to dry anything up. Still at the back of my mind was the nagging question of what these objects had in common.

Half an hour later Penny came back. "How did it go?" she asked.

It was hard to know where to start. I gave a confused account of the conversations.

"What about money?"

"It wasn't mentioned. Holmes 'never varies his fees save where he remits them altogether.' I'm hoping we're in that category. Miss Marple is strictly amateur. Marlowe's rates are $25 a day plus expenses, or used to be in 1943, but he normally gets into a moral tangle and gives the money back. Poirot costs the earth but he seemed to feel sorry for me. I really don't know."

"Mmm. What happens next?"

"They're reporting back in a couple of days."

"All at the same time?"

"That would be fun, wouldn't it?"

Later that day, I realised what all these had in common.

They were all things you didn't buy: you just had them. When did you last buy a tea spoon or a tea towel? Exactly. As for sheets and mugs, they seem to breed. Someone was therefore removing objects that we had been using but not in fact bought. Did this make it a crime? I didn't know.

The tea-spoon situation was becoming critical. None of us takes sugar but they're useful for measuring spices and eating grapefruit, two harmless activities that were now impossible. I realised I had no idea where one bought tea spoons from. Chardonnay, guitar strings, lamb chops, toner cartridges – all these things and more I could find with no trouble. But tea spoons? It was as if I were being confronted with the problem of restocking my life from the basics upwards as a reminder from a higher power that nothing was god-given. I eventually found some in Poundland in Newbury. To be on the safe side, I bought a dozen.

Another possibility struck me when I was discussing it with my son Adam. The thief was softening us up to accept the idea of things disappearing without explanation or apparent motive. Once we were used to this with minor objects we hadn't even bought, larger items going missing wouldn't be seen as odd. A few months hence and we might come back to find a strip from the living room carpet, or all the black notes on the piano, or the top oven, or one of the walls, gone. We'd shrug and say "that's what happens here."

Then there's the feline aspect. This started in July when Nimbus disappeared. Recently we got two kittens. Since then, some tea spoons have reappeared, the mug shelves are filling up and the tea-towel drawer is once again hard to close. I haven't checked the sheets but I've no doubt what I'd find. The number of cats seems important. But how? And why? Above all, is this respite permanent?

No shortage of theories, then, and with more to come when the experts report back. It's been a week now and I haven't heard from them but they're doubtless piecing together this elaborate jigsaw puzzle of deceit and will shortly return to reveal the true culprit. In the meantime, I'm prepared for the next assault from whichever direction it may arrive. Come on, damn you – I'm ready!

Willie, Willie, Harry, Stee

With the extra emphasis now being placed on British history by exam boards and the continuing interest in the royal family's various jubilees, births, marriages, divorces and wrangles, it seemed worth updating the rhyme listing the monarchs since 1066. In the process, we decided to add a few notes about some of the kings and queens in the poem as well as giving a mention to some of those missing from the original.

Willie, Willie, Harry, Stee –
Already, ambiguity:
And so we must at once intrude
Matilda, handsome, proud and rude
Whom Harry said should be his heir,
Though half the barons did not care
To grovel in the Norman dirt
Before a monarch in a skirt.

Harry two – now here's a thing:
Harry's son (called 'the Young King')
Was crowned while dad was still alive
But died before his father: I've
No doubt that future kings did say
'Let's not tempt fate in quite this way.'

Where was I? – Dick (an absentee);
John (a tyrant); Harry three
(Whose only real claim to fame
Was the length of time he reigned).

Then one, two, three Ned, Dick again,
Whom believed was less than sane:
(Shakespeare clearly felt this way –
If in doubt, go see his play).
That was the view of Bolingbroke
Who said, 'It's high time that I took
The crown – a change of century
Needs also a new dynasty
(Though still Plantagenet, it's true.')
So: Harry four, five, six – then who?

Then who? I'll tell you: it was Ned
Who put the crown upon his head.
Note the verb: he won a war
And then proclaimed 'I'm Edward four!'
Til Warwick said 'I'm getting pissed
Off with this vile Yorkist:
A rose of quite a different hue
is needed – Harry six (part two)!'
The barons did not all agree
Some said 'Hen does not seem to be
A monarch who can win this war
So let's get Eddie back once more!'

Right – Edward four, five (though the lad
Was never crowned) then Dick the Bad –
Though not bad if you chance to be
A fan of Leicester C.F.C.
For since this king was re-interred
The team has won (perhaps you heard)
The '15-'16 football crown
And aren't (as some thought) going down.

So – Edward four, five, Dick the Bad
Harry, Harry, Ned the Lad
Then Jane, whose claim was fast disputed
(And was quickly executed).

Mary, Bess (we'd rather not
say aught of Mary Queen of Scots:
For notwithstanding all the years
Since then, it does at times appear
The evil, ghostly silhouette
Of Walsingham is with us yet:
Campbell; Cummings; faces change
But dark intentions stay the same.)

So – back to Bess; then James the Vain
(Who only, I think, gained this name
Because he liked books more than wars
And boys, in general, more than whores.)

Charlie, Charlie, James again
(Another pause I must explain:
The papists and the Jacobites
Do not accept the list is right
From this point on, and would prefer
The Stewart to the Hanover.
They thus have asked I add for you
The two pretenders, old and new:
So this, reluctantly, I do.)

And we must say a word as well
About a certain O. Cromwell
Who, though once tempted by the crown,

Eventually turned it down.
He therefore has no right to be
In any rhyme of royalty:
The more so (if you're taking sides)
As Cromwell was a regicide.
(Richard Cromwell's role's so small
He's not worth mentioning at all.)

Right – Bill and Mary, then came Anne
(Whom some thought was in fact a man)
Four Georges (mostly fat or mad)
Willie (drunk) and Vickie (sad);
Edward, George then Neddy Eight
Who was, I now need to relate,
Not crowned: so purists are averse
To see him in a royal verse:
This man who said he'd rather be
In wedlock with a divorcee
Who was – worse still – both slightly grey
And native to the USA.

And so to George, then Liz the Second
Next to Charlie, so it's reckoned –
Though not by all; indeed some say
'Charlie – king? Oh Christ, no way!
The man's the biggest bore alive –
Let's move straight on to Willie five!'
Some see the opportunity
To terminate the monarchy;
While others plot, with faith and hate,
The advent of a caliphate.

Chas must despair he'll see the day
When, frail and balding, old and grey,
He vows to safeguard all the views
Of Christians, Muslims, Sikhs and Jews
Of every faith, of every kind
And talk to trees, and speak his mind
And, when so moved, proceed to lecture
Us on modern architecture.

In short, he must at times despair
He'll ever be much more than heir;
He must despair he'll ever see
(Given mum's longevity)
His name on coins as Charlie Three.

The Murder at The Three Horseshoes

THIRTEEN CRIME WRITERS were gathered together in a hotel in a small country town. Outside, the wind howled across the mellow rooftops and the wind lashed at the mullioned windows of the ancient coaching inn. Inside, a bright fire was burning in the lounge.

Seven of the novelists, all of whom had that day attended an international crime-writers' symposium, were British. Among them was Jonas Flay, only slowly recovering from a breakdown after spending three years writing a book of such devilish complexity that, by the time he got to the last chapter, he was so confused that he could no longer remember who the murderer was. Also present was Selina Rosencratz, the celebrated creator of Lucy Parker, the five-year-old autistic savant musical prodigy sleuth. Jo Lacemaker was also present, fresh from receiving a garland of awards for *A Question of Self-identity* which featured perhaps the world's first transgender detective. The more traditional form of the genre was represented by Samuel Fforbes-Taylor whose 1920s country-house mysteries had, in the words of one critic, 'done more than anything else to make me want to cancel my membership of the National Trust.' Rufus Raft, Jessie Pankhurst and Tariq Sem are surely well-enough known to require no introduction.

None of these were, of course, their real names.

France had a solitary attendee, the saturnine, etiolated, taciturn Marcel LeFebvre, a leading proponent of the neo-reductivist school, whose novels were described as 'small miracles of Gallic nihilism'. Many of those present doubted that his novels qualified as detective fiction at all as they contained no murders and no policemen and sometimes no characters or dialogue. Presenting a contrast both in literary style and physical appearance was the jovial and corpulent Saxon, Otto Weimar. His novels were long, rumbustious affairs in which the victims, and usually the murderers as well, were senior ecclesiastics. From the USA came the well-known Josh Lashman. His stories featured his hardboiled Marlowe-esque PI Jake Holding attempting to solve complex cyber-crimes and terrorist outrages, so creating a collision of styles which was, according to the *Wyoming Star*, 'akin to listening to a polar bear trying to play the Moonlight Sonata on a mouth organ.'

The other three writers were from Scandinavia, that present-day hot-bed of fictional crime. Jonas Trapp, creator of the deaf sleuth Smilla Tolsvaag, was celebrating the recent translation into Basque of his latest novel, *Come Again*. Ebba Clink was the youngest writer present. Her first novel, of which great things were expected, not least by her, was to be published in 280-character instalments on Twitter in the summer. Finally, who can be unaware of Alix Luftholm: her latest *magnum opus* featured a serial killer whose victims included the entire population of three villages, a feat which the *Upsala Nya Tidning* described as being 'an act of wholesale slaughter unmatched in the annals of popular fiction.'

These, then were the writers gathered together in The Three Horseshoes in Wantbury that fateful night. The symposium was over and the blood-thirsty pensmiths were refreshing themselves liberally at the bar. Intoxication can pass for conviviality in a bad light: however, on this occasion it would have been obvious to any careful observer that all was not well.

The main problem, which affected each writer equally in respect of all the others, was a condition of simmering jealousy. There were now almost as many awards for crime fiction as there were crime novels published, sponsored by organisations as diverse as the West Midlands Serious Crime Squad, Dignitas, Bristol Rovers FC and the World Bank. For each winner in the room there were twelve others who begrudged them their success. As most were the recipients of several awards and as it's a fact that we most covert the prizes that we don't win, the atmosphere was pregnant with a brooding unease.

All the objections were predicated on the idea that the award had in each case been made to X either because of gimmicks in the plot or characterisation which should, in themselves, have disqualified the book from any consideration based on merit; or because bribery, intimidation, nepotism or blackmail had been employed. None of the alliances that formed around each accusation was permanent for each writer was also party to, or the subject of, separate but overlapping groupings with a different author as its target. Only Ebba Clink, who had yet won no awards, was exempt from this and her opinions were not sought. It was, however, widely accepted that anyone who issued their debut novel on Twitter stood accused of gimmickry of the first order. This was despite the fact that two of those present had published a novel on Facebook, one on Instagram and one on the dark web.

The strained atmosphere in the hotel and the dark storm which raged outside. it seemed the perfect and traditional setting for some heinous deed. With thirteen celebrated crime writers in residence it seemed impossible that this opportunity would be passed up.

By midnight, the last of the murder merchants had staggered upstairs to their various beds. Downstairs the tables were cleared and the lights were dimmed. The Night Manager, wearying of these overheard tales of slaughter and deception, settled down in his alcove with a large pot of tea and a copy of *The Wind in the Willows*. Outside, the rain was easing but still the wind howled, as strident and as menacing as the emotions which for the last two hours had been raging in the bar.

The call to the Police Station came in at 2.11am. Within fifteen minutes Inspector Jack Crabtree had parked his 1963 E-Type outside the hotel and he and Sgt Caroline Hastey were knocking on the door. Tom Gold, the ashen-faced Manager, ushered them inside.

"So, sir," Crabtree said when the badges had been flashed, "what seems to be the trouble?"

Gold swallowed once or twice. "There's a room we use for private functions," he began. "We call it the Library, because…because…"

"Because it used to be a library?" Hastey suggested.

"No, no. We just thought it was a good name. It hasn't got any books in it. That's just what it's called."

"Yes, yes," said Crabtree impatiently. His East Midlands accent always became more pronounced when he was angry or in danger of becoming so. "And?"

"As part of my normal rounds, I went in there about half an hour ago. And I found…I found…" He seemed incapable of continuing.

"For Christ's sake," the Inspector said under his breath. "You found *what*, exactly?"

"I found that there was no body in there."

There was a shocked silence.

"Who's staying here tonight?" Crabtree asked. "You have thirteen rooms, is that right?"

"Yes. And we have thirteen crime writers in the hotel."

"Jesus," Crabtree said. He foresaw numerous problems with the investigation. Each writer would have already written the interview, or one like it, a dozen times and so be always a step ahead of him. "All of which makes it pretty bloody surprising that there should be no body, eh Hastey?"

The Sergeant looked about her slightly wildly but said nothing.

"All the guests still in bed?"

"So far as I know. Mind you, thirteen crime writers, a country hotel, two in the morning – they could be *anywhere*."

"Let's have a look at the Library." Gold led them across the hall and through a door with 'The Library' on it. Crabtree nodded. So far, matters could not be clearer.

Gold turned on the light. The room had a large table, capable of seating a dozen or so people. The walls were decorated with hunting prints. Against one wall was a sideboard. On the opposite wall was a large window. Crabtree spent several minutes examining the room.

"These look like bloodstains to me," he said at last, pointing at the carpet.

"We have the local rugby club in once a month," Gold said, "most recently, the day before yesterday. That sort of thing happens quite often."

"And it looks like a heavy object has been dragged across the floor, here."

"Again, that would be the rugby club."

Crabtree nodded, seemingly satisfied. He turned to Hastey with a dry grin. "This is a real snorter and no mistake. Well," he added to Gold, "we'd better get the guests down."

Ten minutes later, twelve writers were assembled in the main lounge. A lot of the bounce had gone out of them. Several were cross and yawning but all traces of tiredness vanished once Crabtree had explained the sensational reason for their having been awakened.

The most immediate reaction appeared to be one of outrage. This confused Crabtree until he realised that it was actually collective embarrassment. The very *idea* of a dead body in the library (even though there was, technically, no library and there was no dead body) was feeble in the extreme. It was monstrous – and possibly actionable, Selina Rosencratz muttered – that they, the cream of their profession, the thrusting vanguard of the neo-noir, should be associated with it, even negatively.

This was followed by a general movement towards the Library but Hastey barred the way. In querulous tones, each explained how their peculiar expertise, insight and knowledge was vital to solving whatever crime had been, or had not been, or might have been, committed. It was so simple; so obvious; why, a child could see through it. Several claimed that they had *already* solved it in half a dozen different ways. LeFebvre said that it was incapable of solution as it was clearly a philosophical and not a criminal issue. Lashman was trying to persuade Tom Gold to sell him a bottle of Scotch. The Scandinavians were talking excitedly in Swedish. Crabtree felt he was losing his grip on the situation. He closed his eyes and took a deep breath.

"There are only twelve of you down here," he said. "Where is the thirteenth?"

They all stopped talking and looked round. Jessie Pankhurst was the first to reply. "Ebba Clink," she drawled.

The writers forgot about the Library and fell to a denunciation of the missing crime-tyro. At last, here was something on which they could all agree. Crabtree could make little sense of what was being said beyond the fact she had done or was about to do something truly awful. Twitter was involved but he couldn't work out how. He looked at his watch: just gone three o'clock. He had been here for barely thirty minutes and again felt unequal to the demands of the investigation. He thought longingly of the company of the supple Latvian twins in Thatchford from whose dual embraces the Chief Inspector's phone call had torn him an hour before.

He was about to appeal for silence and attempt to discover what everyone was talking about when there was a far more dramatic development. The back door which led to the courtyard opened. Everyone fell silent. There, in the doorway, stood the elfin figure of Ebba Clink, dressed only in a yellow nightdress.

"What is going on?" she asked.

Everybody started to explain at once.

Ebba Clink's tinkling laugh cut through the wild hubbub and eventually silenced it. "But that is so *simple* to explain," she said. "I couldn't sleep and came downstairs. I remembered that there was a room marked 'Library' and so thought I might find a book. Instead

I found a man slumped across the table, dead. He had been stabbed in the neck...with a stiletto." All of the writers let out a groan.

"I know," Ebba said, "so crude, so...*clichéd*. I mean, we have a *reputation* to protect, no?" She looked round the room, a faint glint of malice in her eyes. "I know we may not have agreed on everything tonight but this device, this...clumsy incident, would be a *disaster* for us all, would it not?" They all nodded, none more so than Fforbes-Taylor who had always ensured that his country-house victims were murdered anywhere other than in the library, so believing that this helped his plots appear fresh and original.

Crabtree breathed a sigh of relief. At last there was some light in the darkness. "So – what happened to the body, Miss Clink?"

"What do you think?" she asked, her eyebrows raised. "I dragged it out and dumped it in the river." She pointed at the stone floor: un-noticed until now, there were several tell-tale spots of blood leading from the Library to the doorway at which she had recently made her dramatic reappearance. "There was some blood on my dressing gown as well but I burnt that in the incinerator."

Crabtree swung round to Tom Gold. "Is that true?" he asked crisply.

"Oh, yes," the Manager said. "We always have a small incinerator ready whenever we have crime writers staying, just in case."

The Inspector nodded approvingly. "The river's flowing quite fast at the moment, isn't it?"

"Yes," Tom Gold said.

"And the county line is about four miles downstream, where my jurisdiction ends." He thought for a moment. "There are no weirs or obstructions, are there?"

"No," Gold assured him. "The river's quite clear. The last time, at the Pen of Death convention, the body was out of Brockshire within ten minutes."

"Well," Crabtree said after a long pause, "that seems to be that.

I'd like to congratulate Miss Clink on her prompt action. It seems to me," he went on, glancing round the room, "that all you have a good deal to thank her for, newcomer to your circle though she is." No one disagreed. "A convention of cutting-edge, innovative, original crime-writers," he continued slowly, injecting into each word as much sarcasm as he thought it could bear, "and a *body* is discovered, stabbed with a *stiletto*, in a *library*!" Why, you'd have been the laughing stock of your profession." He paused to allow this to sink in. In every face, the Frenchman's most of all, he read the same horror at the thought that they might suddenly have been made to look conventional and staid. The scandal – for scandal it would have been – would have demonstrated a collective failure of creativity on a truly colossal scale. As it was…

"As it is," he concluded, "you're off the hook, as am I. The body is Woldshire's pigeon now." He checked his watch, considering whether the Latvian twins would have waited for him: probably not, as they were paid, in advance, by the hour. "And so, as no crime has been committed that I have any evidence of or which you would choose to write about, I suggest that a small celebration is in order. Mr Gold?"

"Yes?"

"Fourteen pints of lager, if you please, and an orange juice for the Sergeant."

Silver Haze

"YOU'VE DONE *WHAT*?" Mike said.

Gemma looked at him in that blank, unblinking way that she had when dealing with his objections. It rarely failed to work. The lack of visible emotion gave Mike nothing to work with and turned him in on himself. He would then come out like a small boy in the playground, wildly swinging his puny fists against the wrong target.

"I've invited Pearl over. At four. About Dipsy."

Mike pressed his forehead against the kitchen window pane. A misty March sky pressed back against the glass and, for about two seconds, cleared his troubled mind. Then he straightened and the familiar horror film returned – the problems in their relationship; the miscarriage two months before; the hideous debt nightmare with Fat Tom and his ghastly silent friend he'd met in the pub that awful night three weeks ago.

Why had he felt that had been the solution to anything? He hadn't understood multiple compound interest then but did now. Like a virus in a pandemic, the debt seemed to be, in fact was, increasing exponentially. The fact that the five grand had been turned to nothing in one crazy afternoon at Newbury racecourse made the whole thing even more pointless. The debt, he had recently been told, stood at eight grand. He didn't have eight grand.

There was another day of reckoning to come because he hadn't yet told Gemma about this. He pressed his forehead on the window pane again but this time obtained no relief: just the blurred reflection of a middle-class, middle-aged man in a whole heap of shit staring out across what little he could see of his tangled garden and the world that lay beyond it.

Gemma had mentioned this animal whisperer, who was going to tell them why their cat Dipsy had suddenly decided to crap in the hall rather than in the litter tray. He looked down at Dipsy now, stretched out on the kitchen bench, and stroked her back. The cat stiffened and gazed up at him as if expecting a rebuke.

Mike felt a stranger in his own home. He couldn't face this Pearl character, doubtless festooned in kaftans and reeking of patchouli, dropping new-age slogans around while she sucked up the aura and gushed Californian platitudes about Gaia and animal sentience. He had just got Gemma's permission, willingly given, to absent himself from the séance when the doorbell rang.

A normally dressed and completely sane-looking woman stood on the doorstep and held out her hand. "Hi," she said, "I'm Pearl. You must be Mike."

He could think of nothing to say apart from a mumbled "yeah." She smiled, as if this had been all she was expecting, and walked confidently into the house, looking around her as she did so. There were two ways in from their small entrance hall but she chose the correct, right-hand, option and was moments later in air kisses and warm greetings with his wife.

Feeling obscurely wrong-footed in a situation which he had already agreed not to be present at, he slowly followed her into the kitchen and stood hovering by the back door while the two women ignored him.

"So – you're Gemma," Pearl was saying. He remembered now that that they had never met. He had, unlike Gemma, no such gift of instant empathy, even with people he had known for years. With a mumbled apology, he went upstairs to what he called his study.

For two years he had been trying to get a web business off the ground. It was ticking along, producing a measurable though pitiful revenue. He knew he needed a more powerful computer; also that he needed help, particularly with the awful business of social media.

He now could not conceive why he had decided that borrowing money from Fat Tom in the Queen's had seemed such a good way of raising the money; even less, how blowing the whole lot at Newbury racecourse the day after he'd received the cash had seemed like a good way of spending it. He could still recall the triple hangover the following morning, drink, debt and failure fighting for the upper hand. Three weeks – Jesus. How could a life slide from rubbish to completely crap that quickly?

He swung round in his chair and caught sight of the two guitars propped against the wall. Time was when he felt that writing songs would be his way out of the mire. In a moment of madness he'd bought another computer on which to record these insights. He'd never got the hang of it. Whenever he played guitar, which was increasingly rarely, it was the same old song, perhaps the only thing he'd ever written or ever could write. Worse still, he found that he was forgetting simple chord changes and muddling the words. It seemed to him that the song was in any case of no worth. No other songs had been written. Gemma occasionally asked, in a vague way, how his music was going and he would reply equally vaguely. There was nothing to show for all that strumming, nothing to show for the cost of a Strat, an Ibanez Talman, a keyboard, a Mac and a copy of Logic Pro – nothing at all. It was another deception.

He swivelled back round to what he laughingly referred to as his 'work computer' to be faced by an equally awful failure. The website business involved promoting local firms. Having signed a few up, he soon realised he had no ideas, motivation or energy to accomplish this task. He had the fond notion that creating a website would of itself produce magical engagement for anyone featured on it. He saw now that that this required effort, time and skill far beyond what he had devoted to it. The dozen or so clients were starting to ask what evidence there was for their continuation. He could see none. It was for this reason he had borrowed the money, to employ an expert to provide help. This would, so his tangled logic ran, solve the problem with one magic stroke. The money, however, had gone and, as usual, he had nothing to show for it.

Flicking through the menus on his website he came to 'stories'. Before he could stop, he opened *Glory Days*, the tale he had planned to be the first of a series of amusing and thoughtful parables of the modern age. More than just a superior and topical information source, the site was also to be a place for intelligent, amusing and thought-provoking fiction. It would offer insights into the human condition and also self-effacing tales of unfortunate episodes from his own past. Despite the many aspects of his life which deserved such treatment, no further stories of either kind had been created.

Even more of a fiasco had been his resolution to write a wry, jaunty and faintly cynical weekly commentary on local events which would praise unsung heroes and admonish the corrupt or incompetent. The first one, some months ago, had been OK but had relied on paraphrasing a story about a planning application, which he had not really understood, from the local paper. The following the week the paper had been forced to retract it. Mike had not felt the need to retract anything because the post had only got six hits. To have spent several hours plagiarising something that turned out to have been wrong and which hardly anyone had read was doubly, perhaps triply, pointless.

He had continued for a few more weeks but it dawned on him that he knew too little about what was going on in the area and could not motivate himself to find out more. Once, when calling up a local councillor, his nerve had failed before dialling the last digit. He had, in any case, nothing in particular to say about anything. He held no strong views, espoused no causes, supported no campaigns. He was a disconnected man trying to do something that, above all else, required connection. The whole venture was doomed to fail. This in turn made both the decision to borrow the money and the act of blowing it even more pointless. The problem was more than just financial: it proved the ultimate futility of everything he was trying to do, such as it was.

While he was wallowing in these circular and depressing, though essentially accurate, reflections he sensed a changed atmosphere in the kitchen, which was directly under his room. For the last ten minutes or so he had been vaguely aware of what had seemed an ordinary conversation. No exact words had penetrated the ceiling but the dynamics had been clear and normal. Now there were longer pauses. One person appeared upset and the other was trying to reassure her. He realised that the person who was upset was his wife. Although not certain that this was a good idea, he stood up and went downstairs.

The atmosphere had indeed changed. Pearl was looking at the floor, at the cat, out of the window: anywhere but at Gemma, who was sitting upright at the other side of the kitchen table staring slightly wildly at the fridge. Dipsy was hunched on the bench next to Pearl in an attitude more associated with illness. For a moment no one said anything.

Eventually, Gemma shook herself and stood up. "Pearl told me some…interesting things," she said at last. The two women looked at each other for the first time since Mike had arrived. After a moment, Pearl nodded quickly. "I…we think it's best if she told you," Gemma continued. "She's parked up by the church. Perhaps you could walk up there with her."

"OK, fine" Mike said slowly. There was another pause. Pearl stood up and opened her mouth but no sound emerged. Gemma, who at any moment of departure usually managed to start a new conversation, was similarly struck dumb. Eventually Pearl raised her hand in a strange kind of salute and turned away. Mike stepped aside as she turned out of the kitchen and walked towards the front door. He followed her, wondering what the hell was going on.

They turned left and followed the village street, parallel to the river which marked the southern edge of their garden. It's difficult to fall into a companionable step with someone nearly a foot shorter than you, whom you've never met before and who is clearly about to say something unwelcome but Mike did his best.

After about twenty paces, Pearl started to talk.

This probably sounded crazy, she began, but she'd say it anyway and let Mike judge. She explained that she could communicate with animals; could, up to a point, read their thoughts and understand their pre-occupations. Mike nodded. So far they seemed to be on safe, if slightly batty, ground. Then she told him that Dipsy had been upset about the miscarriage.

Mike stopped in the middle of the road. Pearl walked on a couple of paces and then turned to face him. "I know," she said. "You didn't tell anyone about it. Nor did Gemma. She certainly didn't tell me. Dipsy was *devasted*."

"Why?" Mike heard himself asking.

"Because you two were," Pearl said with crushing simplicity.

He looked up and saw that she was crying: not in that tempestuous way he was used to seeing from Gemma; not an intense tropical thunderstorm but a soft, melancholy Irish mist.

This information put a different complexion on everything. Mike was faced with several problems: but these and their solutions – if any existed – were predicated on basic assumptions about how the world worked. One was that animals were not sentient or, if they were, that they could not communicate their sentience to humans. What he had just heard suggested this assumption was wrong. What other assumptions might be wrong as well?

He looked at Pearl again. There was something else coming.

It seemed that Dipsy had also said that, about a week ago, there had been a fresh anxiety, to do with, Pearl had guessed, money. What the cat was upset about was that this had not been shared between the two of them. It was either a financial problem Gemma had got into that she hadn't told Mike about, or – and the inference was obvious – *vice versa*. It was then that the litter-tray problems had begun.

"It's not for me to say what you two should do about this," Pearl said. "If it's true, of course," she added in a rush. I was just asked to say what Dipsy was thinking. And that's what I got.

It was clear to Mike, as it must have been to Gemma, that the knowledge of the miscarriage proved the knowledge of the money. Mike could think of nothing to say.

By this time they had reached the point where the road turned sharply to the right towards the church. Ahead of them was a field, divided into three roughly equal parts with electric fences, each at right angles to the road. The first section had two race horses, one a good deal more elegant and a hand taller than the other. Pearl and Mike paused. After a few moments, both horses came up to the fence, the larger one with greater confidence. Pearl relaxed slightly and rested her hand on its neck. It bowed its head and then looked up, staring, not at Pearl, but at Mike.

His view of animals having been dramatically changed in the last three minutes, Mike met the gaze with a strange candour. He knew something of this animal including its name, its trainer and the fact that the following day at 3.15 it would be under starters orders in a novice chase at Newbury. There was also something else he couldn't put his finger on, some emotion he was unused to feeling.

"He's called Silver," Pearl said gently. This wasn't bad, he thought: the name was in fact Silver Haze. "The other horse is called Rio." She removed her hand from Silver Haze's neck by a few inches. "He loves Rio being around him," she went on, then paused as if she had lost the signal or was getting mixed messages. "I think...yes. If Rio weren't there he wouldn't be able to race at all." She frowned slightly, as if briefly confused by the information. She withdrew her hand.

Silver Haze fixed Mike with another deeply knowing stare. Again, Mike felt faintly overwhelmed, his mind briefly full of strange images and ideas.

Pearl turned to face Mike. Her mood, now she'd communicated with an animal that seemed to have nothing to do with him, was lighter. "He's racing tomorrow, apparently."

"Oh, really?" Mike said.

Silver Haze's eyes held Mike's for a few more seconds. Then he flicked his head and spun away across the field. Rio followed him.

Pearl and Mike walked up towards the car park by the church. Neither of them said anything until she had got into the car. Mike's hand rested on the door frame, preventing her from closing it.

"Well – thank you," Mike said.

She nodded and put the key in the ignition.

"I…" Mike began.

Pearl had shut her eyes. "Like I said, I'm just telling you what I get. Don't…"

"Shoot the messenger?" Mike suggested.

She shrugged: then, as a final gift, gave him a smile. "Perhaps that." Mike took his hand off the door and she closed it. Then he was giving her a wave as she pulled away, turned right and was gone.

Mike slowly waked back home. He was clearly due a serious chat with Gemma. Although she was of a generous and forgiving nature, the act of concealing the loan and its aftermath from her had made her seem part of the problem. His earlier reflections had shown him that the problem was in fact himself. The idea had not yet taken deep enough root to enable him to do anything about it. Instead, he still felt that one stroke of fortune, however ill-deserved, could turn everything round. He needed something like eight grand to get back to where he had been two weeks ago, before he'd met Fat Tom. Granted, that wasn't a great place but it was a damned sight better than the place he was in now.

It was exactly this thought that made him slow down as he walked down past the field. A plan was forming in his mind. He looked at the arrangement of the fences dividing the field into three and noted that there was a little gate about half way along from the first, where the horses now were, to the second and another that led into the third. The perimeter fence itself seemed simple enough. He walked home in a state of mounting excitement.

The brief chat with Gemma was a bit grim. He said that, yes, he *had* had money worries recently and had been talking to the bank since exactly the time Pearl had said. She asked him why he hadn't shared this with him. He said he hadn't wanted to bother her and that the whole thing had gradually been building up over the last ten days. This was the worst lie and, that having been accepted, or at least not challenged, he felt he'd got away it. Everything should be turning a corner soon, he said, he was sure of it. All the bullshit surrounding this would need to be confronted at some point but that could wait. What he needed, and seem to have achieved, was 24 hours to put this latest plan into action.

It was clear Gemma only half accepted this guff but she didn't seem up to having a full-scale showdown there and then. Pausing only to give Dipsy a cuddle, from which the cat once again recoiled, he dashed upstairs to execute Operation Silver Haze.

The first task was a glance at the form for tomorrow's 3.15 novice chase at Newbury. It couldn't have been better. Silver Haze was the hot favourite at even money, followed by Murphy's Law at 4/1, the oddly-named Masked Cottager at 8/1 and a long list of the rest nowhere. This could change, of course, but the relative positions seemed assured. The market had agreed on the front runners. He hoped the market was right.

Next, he examined his immediately realisable assets. This was less encouraging. Perhaps £2,500 was available but to clear all of that would result in a bill for the web hosting, inconveniently due tomorrow, to bounce. Two grand should do it. Two bank cards and a trip to Hungerford to get the cash would be needed. There were two bookies in Hungerford. That took care of that.

Then he went downstairs and changed into some dark clothes and put in his pockets a torch and half a dozen sugar cubes. He went back upstairs 'to do some urgent emails' as he told Gemma. In fact, he stared out of the window, waiting impatiently for dusk to fall across the valley. This it did, in the way of watched pots and sunsets in high latitudes, agonisingly slowly.

At seven o'clock, Gemma had a conference call with one of her committees. These never lasted less than an hour. At two minutes to he went back downstairs and put his coat. "I'm just popping down the Queen's to meet Mark," he said. She was already fiddling with the connections on her laptop and nodded abstractedly. "Says he might have someone to help me with the social media."

He realised as he was saying it that this was a lie too far, the kind of thing that could be checked up on later and require a further lie, and perhaps Mark's connivance, to get out of. Another problem for tomorrow. "Pesto pasta OK? I'll do it when I get back." She nodded vaguely again.

He left the house but, instead of turning right to the pub, turned left, retracing the route he'd taken with Pearl a few hours before. It was by now pitch dark and quite cold. A dog-walker passed him but an anonymous 'hi' was sufficient at that time of day. As he got to the bottom corner of the field, where the road up to the church turned to the right, it got darker still as all the houses on the other side of the road were shielded behind hedges. Mike took a deep breath. Time to get to work.

He suddenly felt a lot less brave. Felonies of uncertain gravity would start as soon as he crossed the fence. He wondered if he had been wise to trust the apparent lack of security devices in a fairly deserted field that contained valuable racehorses. He had not checked to see if there were floodlights or, worse still, somehow ensured there was no secret alarm that would alert the trainer or the police. He wished now that he were drunk and coming from the opposite direction: he could then claim that, *en route* back from The Plough a mile or so up the valley with a skinful of beer, he'd decided to try a short cut across the field. Should he now go home and get drunk, then start again? But he'd told Gemma he was going to the Queen's, in the opposite direction. This had only been five minutes ago. Hardly time to go to The Plough instead, get drunk, and then walk back. Plus, anyone at The Plough would say he hadn't been there. So that wouldn't work.

He tried to clear his head. This was nonsense, picking holes in a stupid alibi he hadn't even been asked for. He took a deep breath. Now or never. Now. He climbed up over the fence and dropped down lightly on the other side. The crime had begun.

Another problem that he hadn't considered until then was how he would find the horses. The field was about two hundred yards square: even though the horses were only in one of the three sections, he had no idea where they were. He realised he knew nothing about horses apart from the fact that they ran around racecourses. He had some idea that they slept standing up. If true, would this make them more or less easy to surprise? Did he in fact want to surprise them at all? Surprise was probably the last thing he needed. He would be no match for a powerful animal with hard hooves that could run faster than him. Stealth was what was required. He needed to creep up on them…no he didn't. They had had far more efficient predators than him creeping up on them for the last five million years. They were wise to every feeble trick he could employ. He needed to win their trust. That was it. But how could win their trust when he didn't know where they were?

At that moment, events were taken out of his hand when he heard a galloping of hooves coming towards him. He had no time to panic. Suddenly two horses were in front of him: vast, prehistoric shapes now visible to his night eyes, butting, pressing and nudging him like an old friend. He smiled to himself. Another thing he now remembered about horses was that were sociable. This was, after all, the idea on which this plan was based. They were also well-disposed to humans. And here was a human, suddenly arrived in their field.

Even in the quarter-moonlight, Silver Haze was easy to identify by the jagged white flash on his nose. Mike took a sugar cube from his pocket and offered it. Rio pushed and nudged but it was clear who the dominant partner was. Mike took a few paces back, then offered another. This time, only Silver Haze followed, turning to give a whinny to its companion that sounded like a warning. It seemed to be interpreted as such. As he moved towards the centre of the field, Silver Haze was still following him but Rio's sad profile vanished into the gloom.

More by luck than planning, a few paces later he found himself about to rub against the electric fence that divided the first part of the field from the second. He was reaching to get his torch to see where the gate was when Silver Haze gave him a shove with his nose. He stepped back a few paces. The gesture was repeated. He looked down to his left and, his eyes now attuned to the darkness, saw the gate a few feet behind him. It was just a question of pulling up a catch on the plastic wire and pushing about four foot of the fence, which was hinged, to open the entrance.

He went through and Silver Haze followed him. He shut it behind him and gave the horse the final sugar lump. Remembering that the two openings were conveniently opposite each other, he then led the horse down the field until they came to second wire. In the same way, Silver Haze was introduced into the third part of the paddock. He shut the second gate behind him.

He gave the horse a pat on the nose and walked quickly to the perimeter of the field that ran parallel to the two internal fences.

He climbed over and was back in the world of legal activity, on the footpath that ran between the churchyard and the field and which led back to the to road up which he had earlier walked with Pearl.

No one was around. Quickening his pace, he cut along the side of another field and back down into the centre of the village. Five minutes later he was in the Queen's sinking a pint and asking the barman if someone called Mark had been in asking for him. He then pretended to make a phone call and was back home boiling the water for the pasta before Gemma had finished her conference call. The rest of the evening passed without incident.

The following day he went into town, withdrew the cash and went straight across the road to the two bookies shops which were huddled next to each other near the railway bridge. In each he placed £1,000 on Murphy's Law to win. There didn't seem to be much of a market for the fixture: at the first he got yesterday's odds of 4/1 and the second at slightly improved ones of 9/2. Then he drove home, feeling slightly light-headed.

"Someone called Tom called," Gemma said when he got back. "Said he'd call again. Said he met you in the Queen's a couple of weeks ago."

It took Mike a moment to realise that she was talking about Fat Tom, though he doubted he answered to this name, except violently. His mate had said nothing so he didn't know what he was called. How the hell had he got the number?

"OK," he said as if this news was expected; which, one way or another, it was.

It was just gone two. Work of any kind was impossible. After 20 minutes of moving items around on the Mac desktop, he decided to go for a walk. Inevitably, his footsteps were drawn towards the field near the church.

Rio was there, wandering around helplessly. So too was Paul, the husband of Silver Haze's trainer; confusingly called Pauline. Paul knew Mike as they'd got to the final of a doubles pool competition in the village hall a few months ago. Mike waved. Paul, who had just finished talking to a teenage girl who Mike thought was Paul's daughter, turned and raised his hand. He walked over to where Mike was standing. He seemed preoccupied.

"How's tricks?" Mike asked.

"So-so," Paul confessed. He started rolling a cigarette. "Had a domestic with Milly," he said, indicating the girl.

She was flouncing off, pony-like, towards the far end of the field, vaguely followed by Rio, who seemed to have no other purpose in life apart from being permanently a couple of steps behind someone else. Without looking back, she went through the gate, closed it behind her, and turned right towards Paul and Pauline's house beyond the church. Rio stood still and sad for a moment and then, catching sight of two humans at the other side of the field, trotted hopefully towards them.

"Bloody strange thing," Paul was saying. He turned to indicate the divisions of the field Mike knew all too well. "Silver was in this section last night and this morning he was in that one. Paulie damn near pulled him today. He's in the novice chase at Newbury."

"Oh, really?" said Mike.

"Comes damn close to tampering. We looked him over and he seemed OK. Milly's the only one that tends to come in here. So I asked her." Mike could imagine the question hadn't been phrased with any great delicacy. "She lost it with me. Teenagers, eh?"

Mike muttered some reply.

"Don't suppose you saw anything?" His eyes had narrowed slightly. Mike suspected a trap.

"No," he said. "I did walk up here a couple of times yesterday, once with a friend, once a…a bit later. I didn't see anything odd."

"Thing is," Paul went on, more reflectively, "if Silver's moved around by anyone he doesn't know, he starts whinnying. We'd have heard it. We heard nothing. The mysterious incident of the horse in the night time, eh?"

Mike vaguely recalled the reference. "What?" he said.

"Exactly," Paul said, who wasn't so easily deprived of a punchline. "The horse did bloody well nothing in the night time, apart from being led."

At this point Rio had shimmied up to them. He was standing next to Paul but was looking at Mike with a strangely fixed and, it seemed to Mike, un-equine expression. Paul absent-mindedly reached up and patted his neck.

"So," he went on, "the person knew Silver. That's the way I see it."

"Or the horse wanted to go…" Mike felt himself saying. He tried to bite back his words. He found himself staring at Rio in a way that would, if Paul had been paying him any particular attention, have seemed odd. There was a brief communion between him and Rio. No words passed: merely, as before, a fleeting set of images as if from a dream and a strange wash of emotions that seemed to tell an unexpected story in a fractured language.

"Eh?" Paul asked.

"Excuse me," Mike said and turned away. A few paces later, he looked back and saw Rio still staring at him, his head slightly on one side, his eyes great dark pools.

There was no mistake, Mike realised. He'd been conned.

He went back home and logged on to the *Racing Post* website. There was an awful inevitability about what was going to happen. At 3.25 it was confirmed. Silver Haze had won by 14 lengths.

It was as well that Mike didn't live in Alabama or the Ukraine because, if so, there would probably have been a gun in the house and he'd have loaded it up, gone up to the end of the garden and shot himself. It wasn't so much the money – he reckoned he was probably ten grand down, in addition to all his regular financial problems – but the unremitting failure. The three recent financial deals had been inspired respectively by a fat stranger in a pub, several weasely bookmakers at Newbury Racecourse, and a horse. This was a bad craziness which, superimposed on everything else, went beyond mere bad luck. His life was turning into a car crash.

As for that business with Rio, something was at work that he had neither anticipated nor understood. He wasn't yet sure if he welcomed it. He had an a brief image of himself in a field with a divining rod, finding his hands pulled away from the path he was following by some force he couldn't control.

By now it was nearly five o'clock. There was one place Mike was drawn to so, with leaden steps, he retraced the familiar few hundred yards to the field.

A horse box was just pulling away from the far gate and he saw Silver Haze being released into the field. Rio cantered up to greet him and they nuzzled for a moment. Then they started to trot across towards him, Rio as ever half a length behind.

Mike became aware of someone standing next to him. He turned and found himself looking at Pearl. He realised now how cold it had become. He was wearing only a thin shirt; she had several layers including a puffa jacket. Her face was slightly red. This strangely made her seem rather more attractive than she had done yesterday, though why such irrelevant thoughts were pouring into his mind he couldn't say. He looked up at the setting sun sinking into a dark cloud. The colours were unlike anything he had seen before. Indeed, the whole world seemed to shimmer slightly as if shifting slightly on its axis.

"I thought you'd be here," Pearl said slowly. Mike nodded. The horses had reached the edge of the field. Silver Haze was a few yards behind Rio, shifting slightly from hoof to hoof.

What happened next was relayed to Mike twice: once by Pearl's words but also a second or so later, in a way similar to what he had earlier experienced with Rio. It was if he were suddenly bilingual and was hearing, out of phase, two versions of the same event in two different languages.

"I'm afraid Silver lied to you," Pearl said. "He loves Rio to be with him, but not the night before a race. He needs to be in a zone. He loves winning. Companionship puts him off. Pauline doesn't realise this. Silver wants to win." There was a pause, during which the other part of this news slotted into place. Neither human nor horse had moved an inch.

"He says that he told you the opposite because…"

Mike held up his hand.

"Because," he continued, more hesitantly, "he knew I needed something and thought that he could get me to do this…for bad reasons." There was a long pause. "And he's ashamed." Mike walked forward and held out his hand. "You shouldn't be, Silver," he said gently. "It was all *my* fault. *I'm* the one that should be ashamed." Slowly the horse moved forward until Mike could rest his hand on his head. He felt a surge down his arm, like a benign electric shock. "I'm sorry. And, you might not believe this, but I'm *glad* you won. You deserved it." Silver Haze slowly bowed his head.

Mike removed his hand. The world sunk back into the familiar grey, March dusk; a mist had descended; the horses were fading away. From the houses at the end of the road a few lights twinkled.

Mike and Pearl turned away from the field and walked down towards the centre of the village in a companionable silence.

"I guessed what had happened," Pearl said. "Actually, in fact, I…I knew. So…"

"I know," he said.

"You've got it, you know," she said after a few more paces.

He knew what she meant but, slightly shocked, said nothing.

"Yes, you have. You can communicate. You understood what Silver was saying as clearly as I could. And I've trained for God knows how long."

Mike laughed. "But I had something to help focus my mind – you know, this...fiasco, as it turned out to be. I needed to rely on it. It let me down. Very badly. My fault. But it showed me something I would never have seen otherwise." He paused in the road.

By now the light was almost gone so he could barely see Pearl's expression. It didn't really matter what her expression was. He just had to say it.

"I've been looking for something to change my life." He could say no more.

"And has it?" she asked.

Then he once again became full of doubt, as he had long been, just as he had long been greedy, lazy and self-pitying. What had he done to merit this epiphany?

As if reading his thoughts, Pearl said: "Sometimes things like this just happen."

"But what have I done to deserve it?"

"Nothing, it seems. But that's not the way it always works. You might just have got what you need, though. *Carpe diem.*"

"I..." Mike began; but at that point he recognised a familiar shape round his ankles. It was Dipsy. They were, he now realised, a few yards from their drive. A large and unfamiliar car was parked there. He stared down at Dipsy for a few moments.

"Shit," he said, "Fat Tom's just turned up." Pearl said nothing. He picked Dipsy up, who immediately and uncharacteristically climbed onto his shoulder. "Come in," Mike said to Pearl. "I need to deal with all this. *Carpe diem.*"

They crunched across the gravel drive and under an archway to see a large, round-faced man about to press the bell. In his right hand was a lead, on the other end of which was an angry looking large dog of indeterminate breed which started growling as soon as he saw Mike. Dipsy, normally terrified of dogs, made no particular move apart from tightening her claws slightly on Mike's shoulder.

Mike took a couple of steps forwards and glanced down at the dog. It stopped growling and sat down with his tongue hanging out. Dipsy started purring.

Tom looked from dog to man, from man to cat and from cat to someone else in a puffa jacket standing in the shadows.

"Hello, Tom," Mike said.

There was a silence, broken only by the throbbing of Dipsy's increasingly powerful purrs.

"I think you should treat Tiger a bit better," Mike went on.

"What?" Tom said, completely wrong-footed. "How do you know he's called Tiger?" Instinctively he gave a pull on the lead. Tiger bared his teeth, this time at Tom. The grip was relaxed.

Mike, still with Dipsy on his shoulder stepped forward and touched Tom lightly on the shoulder. "Never mind that. Come in," he said. "Everyone – come in, and let's sort this out."

The Last Turkey in the Shop

FRIDAY WAS THE day Ricky's girlfriend left him. It was also the day he started at Goldswan Trading. These two events were connected.

The advert in the *Evening Standard* had asked a direct question. 'Do you,' it said, 'want to earn £3,000 a week and drive a Porsche?' Ricky decided that he did. 'If so, phone Asif.'

"Could I speak to Asif? About the job."

"Who?"

"Asif. I want to earn £3,000 and drive a Porsche."

"Oh, *that* job. Come in at, er, at three tomorrow."

"Next week I'm going to earn £3,000 and drive a Porsche," he told Jane.

"The hell you will," she said, and slammed the door.

Goldswan Trading was in a converted warehouse building in Shoreditch. Ricky noted that it was called Goldswan House, which sounded rather grand.

The interview took place in a windowless room with nothing in it apart from two chairs and, in the corner, a large refrigerator. A single naked light bulb hung from the ceiling.

"Asif couldn't make it," the man said, "I'm Geoff Partridge, Senior International Sales Manager." He paused to let this dazzling title sink in. Ricky tried to look impressed.

Geoff Partridge talked about the prodigious commission earned by members of his 'team'. Occasionally he asked Ricky questions but rarely paused to listen to the reply.

Ricky wondered if he was going to learn about the job itself. Seemingly it involved selling in some way – but what, and to whom? For all he knew the place could have been a gay brothel.

"So, the..." he began.

At that moment the door opened and a man squeezed into the room. He was dragging a sack. Without apology or explanation he tipped a heap of frozen meat onto the floor and began forcing them into the fridge.

This required either a ten-minute explanation or none at all: Geoff Partridge chose the latter. "You can start tomorrow," he said after the man had left.

"Fine," Ricky said, trying to sound blasé.

"I got the job," he said to Jane that evening.

"What is it?"

Ricky considered this, trying to piece together the few solid facts yielded by the interview.

"Selling meat," he said at last.

"Meat? Who to?"

Ricky groped for one of Geoff Partridge's sonorous phrases. The man had been fond of 'the international trade worldwide', so he tried that. He was amazed how glib he sounded. Even the tautology lent spurious dignity to the remark.

"Sounds like an abattoir."

"I'll sell other things as well. On the phone. Internationally, of course."

"I give it a week."

The following morning, Ricky met Pete, his Australian sales manager. Pete told him what Goldswan did.

"We *sell*."

"Ah. What, exactly?"

"Anything – anywhere, any place, any time, anyhow..." He waved his hand, like a conjurer, as if to include all other words beginning with 'any'. Ricky tried to think of one.

"And 'to anyone'?" he hazarded.

"Exactly." Pete nodded, man-to-man. Ricky smiled back on this new level. The remark seemed to be the key into the heart of the Goldswan organisation.

"And you're going to be a player in the team," he went on, leading Ricky by the elbow into the lift. "We're going to get along." Pete stabbed at the button and the machine shuddered into life. Ricky speculated whether these remarks were designed by way of threat or encouragement.

The doors slid open and they stepped into a room with about thirty desks in rows and one large one at the end. It reminded him of his school except that if it had been at school everyone wouldn't have been chain-smoking and screaming into telephones. "This is your desk. That's John. He'll get you started."

"I'll tell you what," John said as Pete strutted back to his desk, "this place is a shambles." His remarks were delivered out of the corner of his mouth in an annoyingly conspiratorial way. John was forty-three and by a long way the oldest person on the sales floor. "Never known business so bad. I give it three months. I haven't earned a penny here since October."

Ricky made an attempt to rally himself from this deadening world-weariness. This was his new job, his new career. He was going to earn three thousand pounds and drive a Porsche, starting now.

"Could you tell me what I'm selling, and to whom?" he asked.

John didn't have the energy to laugh, so he sneered instead. "What a shambles," he said again.

There was a whoop of delight from the far corner of the room: fists punched the air, backs were slapped. "What's the deal?" a voice called out.

"Only the two dozen Blenheim cat baskets to Iceland, full rate-card," yelled the salesman. A moment later he was caught in a head-lock by Pete who began marching him round his desk. "I knew you could do it, you old bastard. Yeaaaaah!" He slapped the salesman, quite hard, on the cheek: a pair of spectacles shot across the room. There was a burst of husky male applause. "Get the money *on the board*," Pete went on. '£1,700' was entered next to the name of Kasim: there were plenty of names but few other figures. The atmosphere had noticeably improved. Even Ricky was slightly touched by it. He looked at John, who was lighting a small cigar.

"They'll probably cancel," John said. Ricky felt his fragile new-found confidence evaporate.

Pete climbed onto his desk, and gestured for silence. Everyone settled down, looking at expectantly up at the young demagogue.

"I've got one thing to say to you bastards," he began, lighting a Marlboro in the way marines light flamethrowers, "If Kasim can do it you all can. He's an Arab selling cat baskets to Eskimos. Tough pitch, man. When I started – and remember I'm just a no-good ignorant Australian –" he made a self-deprecating gesture to calm the laughter – "I was selling toothpaste to Egyptian architects. And how much did I do in my first week? Five hundred tubes? No. A thousand tubes? No. I'll tell you. Seventeen hundred and sixty tubes, at one pound eighty each. That's more than any of you have done this week. What's the problem? You've got your leads. You've got your phones. Do you all know how to use a telephone?"

There were a few grunts.

"Louder! I can't hear you! *Do you know how to use your phones*?"

"Yes!" everyone except Ricky and John roared with one voice.

"Well *use* them! Look at this board. It's a bloody disgrace. I'll tell you what. Just to show I'm a regular guy, if everyone gets a deal in today, I'll have the Union Jack tattooed on my arse." Even Ricky joined the gasp of amazement. The Australian surveyed the room, revelling in the attention. "That means *everyone*. Including the new guy over there, I can't remember your name but I'm sure you're a lovely bloke, okay. Yeah, you too."

Everyone turned and stared at Ricky. He tried to show by his expression that he expected no special favours.

"Come on then! What are we waiting for, guys?" He jumped lightly off the desk. "*On those phones!*"

Ten minutes later Ricky found himself dialling the number of a shoe shop in Cape Town. There was about twenty seconds of clicks and buzzes and the occasional sad squeak like the noise of a small animal in a trap. He was about to hang up when the line crackled into life.

"Vorster's Shoes."

Ricky pounced. "Good morning, sir."

"Good morning."

"Yes." Ricky scanned his script and selected a line at random. "Do you feel you are adequately protected against malaria?"

"We do not have malaria here," the voice said. "Who is this?"

Ricky tried to marshal his thoughts. If true, this was a setback to the plan of selling two thousand chloroquine tablets. He moved on to the next item.

"How about fires? Fires can break out any time…any place, any time, anywhere and…and anyhow," he finished lamely.

There was a long silence. "Indeed," the man said carefully.

"So maybe you'd be interested in fire extinguishers instead," Ricky said with a flourish. He felt that this defence-into-attack manoeuvre had been rather neat.

"Instead of what?"

"Instead of the…of the…" He tried to remember the name of the tablets: chloro-something. "Instead of the chlorine tablets," he stammered.

"I don't have a swimming pool," the voice replied. "I'm a poor man."

This remark seemed so irrational Ricky suspected it must be some kind of code, part of the dark freemasonry of international tele-sales. He attempted a hearty laugh.

"Aren't we all?" he said, scanning the next sheet of paper in search of a glib line to get him out of this corner. "However, I do have knives."

"Knives?" the man said, his voice expressing an apprehension Ricky interpreted as interest.

"Sharp kitchen knives. Choppers, carving knives, serrated bread knives with reverse razor edges...even small axes and machetes. Plenty of knives."

There was a strangled cry from the other end. "I don't want any trouble," the voice whimpered.

"Who does?" Ricky asked, leaning back in his seat. He felt on a roll. "Who needs trouble? We're talking knives here."

"Urghhh," the man appeared to say.

Ricky leaned back slightly too far and only saved himself from crashing to the floor by slamming his feet under the lip of the desk. Still gripping the receiver, he managed to push himself so that his forehead smashed into his desk light. The metal shade reverberated to a perfect D sharp: a second later the bulb exploded.

"Aaaargh!" said Ricky.

"Urghhh," the man said again.

"Sorry about that," said Ricky, the quicker of the two to regain his composure, "I've got a new electric phone and it shot off across the desk." He paused, wondering why he had told such an unnecessary and elaborate lie. From the other end there was only the sound of panting.

"Hello?"

"Urgh."

Ricky was gripped with the conviction that this was *the* moment to Close That Sale. He held the initiative. Blood pounded in his ears, the thrill of the chase was upon him. Grabbing a script, he roared his closing speech into the mouthpiece. The other salesmen fell silent. Emboldened, Ricky redoubled his efforts, pounding the desk with his fist to emphasise the important features, the easy payment terms, the free delivery. Aggressively, he stood up, the better to lend emphasis to his final sentence.

"Mr Vorster," he bellowed, "the people at Carlsberg say they have 'probably' the best lager in the world: I can promise you we have *definitely* the best cat baskets!"

There was a gasp and a squark from Cape Town, followed by a click-buzz as the connection was cut. Ricky looked up and realised that everyone was gathered round his desk. John raised a sarcastic eyebrow. There was a long pause.

"No budget," Ricky said.

Everybody drifted back to their desks and Ricky allowed himself time to unwind. Something had gone terribly wrong at the end of the conversation but he couldn't put his finger on it...of course – cat baskets. He was *meant* to be selling knives, but the last bit was from the *cat baskets* script. Obviously that was why the man hadn't bought anything. He'd been confused.

Ricky sat back in his seat. On reflection, 'confused' was probably understating it. There were several permutations of horror which his references to fire, disease and sharp instruments could have created. And what could the man have made of the incongruous, culminating, mention of cat baskets? Ricky sniggered at the thought of this traumatised Afrikaner cobbler, never again able to pass a pet shop without having to cross the road in a cold sweat.

After lunch, Ricky was given a list of Bulgarian pharmacists and a script which would enable him to sell them 200-kilo drums of copper-tungsten cable. The document's rationale as to why they might wish to do this contained jumps of logic so prodigious that the only chance of a sale lay in convincing them they were actually buying something else. To assist in this deception, after a few calls he pretended to be French. By quarter to five he was exhausted, but no richer than he had been at nine thirty.

"See what I mean," John said. "Dead. Never known it so bad."

At the other end of the room, Ricky noticed Geoff Partridge, his interviewer from the previous day, locked in conversation with Pete by the sales board. He turned on his heel and stalked down one of the rows of desks. His face was dark with rage, reawakening in Ricky the sensation of being back at school.

"Right!" Geoff Partridge suddenly shouted, "I've had enough. This is the worst team in the company by a mile and a quarter. Look at that total, sixteen-two-fifty. It stinks. OK – no one sits down until we've got to twenty grand. On your feet! Up! Sally!" A frightened young woman appeared at the office door. "Sally, get these chairs cleared away. Now!"

Grumbling only slightly, twenty-five grown men lumbered to their feet. Sally moved among them, her eyes averted.

"And get that window open! *All* the windows! Jesus, everyone here's *fast asleep!*" Gusts of icy December air billowed across the office, gradually dispersing the fug of stale smoke, body odour and evaporated testosterone. "You too," he said roughly to Pete. "Set an example, if you can. Come on, everyone – *on those phones*! I want to hear the *money* coming in!"

The babel of voices reached a crescendo. Ricky dialled a Vienna number and waited, shivering.

"*Dan dragenhosen rumpenpumpen in die wormingcatz gropentopen*," the voice seemed to say. Softly, Ricky hung up. The whole thing was quite hopeless.

At the other end of the room, Pete was setting an example.

"How can you say you're not ill, Mr Jones?" he was shouting at some unfortunate stranger. A Paraguayan vet? A Danish butcher? It was more than likely Pete didn't know himself. Ricky suspected most people were dialling numbers at random. As Geoff Partridge's venomous gaze briefly fixed itself on him, Ricky did the same.

"The time, sponsored by Accurist..."

"And I'm telling you you're a sick man," Pete went on. "You may not know it, but you're *very* ill. But, hey, you're lucky, Mr Jones. I have the drugs to cure your condition. Seventeen hundred pounds for a year's supply, and let me tell you, Mr Jones, you can't get these on prescription, oh no. Until this moment in time they've only been available to NASA for combatting the effects of weightlessness in outer space."

"... five...twenty-five...and twenty seconds." Ricky put down the phone. The scene was acquiring many of the characteristics of a nightmare.

A few minutes later there was a wild howl of joy: twelve dozen ornamental tea-caddies were on their way to St Lucia. The total stood at nearly eighteen thousand pounds. There followed a brief honeymoon period of renewed activity: then, as the cold again started to bite, enthusiasm and confidence again waned.

"I can stay here all night," Geoff warned them. The hands of the clock inched their way towards five-thirty.

Just as it seemed impossible that the foundations of Goldswan House could withstand any more noise, Pete slammed down the phone and leaped into the air. "Done it, done it!" Everyone roared with relief and hung up without bothering even to finish their sentences. "Five Cousteau fish tanks to Dar-es-fucking-Salaam. What a result!" The congratulations that followed would have put a last-minute FA Cup Final goal to shame. Even Ricky felt sufficiently moved to shake his Pete's hand through the melée.

"They'll probably cancel," John said.

Geoff Partridge, from a being figure of terror, now transformed himself into a jovial Father Christmas. Champagne appeared from somewhere, jokes were exchanged, backs were slapped.

Geoff slipped out of the room, reappearing a few minutes later with a heavy sack over his shoulder. This prompted a verse of *Jingle Bells* sung in several different keys.

"Now – with Christmas coming up I know you're all looking

forward to stuffing something," he began, to a chorus of 'ooo-er', "so I've got you all some raw material." He tipped the sack onto the floor, releasing a cascade of semi-thawed poultry. "One each, come on, there you are...a nice big one for you, you don't look like you're getting enough – come on, who hasn't got one?"

Soon everyone had a turkey in their hand. Ricky's looked more like a vulture, with a long, dangling neck and strangely dark flesh. He pressed his nose to the plastic wrapping. It smelled faintly of disinfectant.

"And now," Geoff was saying, "this week's big prize for this week's prize guy – Kasim!" Everyone clapped and whooped. Kasim was pushed to the front, blushing like a schoolboy. "Bring in the big prize, Sally."

From the corridor there came the sound of someone trying to lift a heavy object. The door inched open, revealing a tantalising glimpse of naked pink flesh: then there was a crash and an oath. Finally, Sally appeared, her hair awry. She was half carrying, half dragging, a frozen pig.

Kasim's eyes widened in amazement. "Apple up its arse, few roast potatoes and there's your Christmas dinner sorted," Geoff Partridge suggested.

John strolled up to Geoff. "Any chance of any actual money?" he asked.

"Money? Money? No one's hit their targets."

"The targets keep going up."

"That's inflation, boyo. You're lucky." He raised his voice. "You're all lucky." The salesmen had been comparing turkeys, but now they all looked at Geoff. "You're so lucky that we're letting you work on territories sometimes with a thousand per cent inflation. Your rate card doubles during the conversation. The quicker the guy signs, the more money he saves." Several people laughed, others looked seriously attentive: no one was willing to challenge his economics.

"What an angle!" He turned back to John. "That's the way I'd look at it if I were you. Anything else you'd like to complain about?"

"Muslims don't eat pork," John said.

"The hell they don't. That's Jews."

"And Muslims."

"Whatever. Well, you can swop it for these." He thrust a packet of lamb chops into his hand. "It'll be the first deal you've done for weeks. Happy Christmas."

"We used to get paid," John said to Ricky after Geoff Partridge had swept out of the room, "in the old days." He made the time seem infinitely remote.

"What's happened since?"

"Obvious, isn't it?"

Ricky thought about it for a moment. "No."

"They've run out of money. This is all they've got to give us."

£3,000 a week plus a Porsche paid in frozen meat would certainly take some storing. He looked down at his own wages, estimating it would probably cost about £4.50 in Tesco. The animal had a sad, last-turkey-in-the-shop look about it. He wondered what he was going to do with it.

"I'd throw that away, if I were you," John said, reading his thoughts. "It's probably contaminated. Last Friday, it was boxes of chocolates we got. Big ones. I took mine home to the wife, and the first one she bit into, do you know what she found?"

Ricky didn't want to know but couldn't think of a way of saying so.

"A tooth, a human tooth. A molar. And the next one..."

"Who's coming to the pub?" a voice interrupted.

John shook his head. "I don't drink," he said to Ricky. "I was on two bottles of scotch a day. My gums used to bleed." He pulled back his upper lip, revealing a set of yellowing teeth. "See, they don't any more, look."

Ricky joined the drift round to the Star and Garter. The place was packed, mostly with people from the sales floor, easily identifiable because they all carried turkeys. It was hard to see what they had to celebrate.

"Chickens in the basket!" Pete was shouting. The landlord passed among the drinkers collecting the turkeys, offering a smile here, a joke there. Perhaps it was because Ricky was unfamiliar or perhaps his turkey was not flourished with enough bravado, but the basket passed him by. He felt pleased. It was hardly a permanent trophy for the day's work, unless he were to have it stuffed and mounted in the living room, but it deserved a better fate that this. He cradled it like a cat, gently stroking the cellophane wrapping with his index finger.

Haggling between Pete and the landlord eventually resulted in eighty pounds cash and a hundred pounds on a slate behind the bar. A few people took their meagre share of the proceeds and drifted away. Lager was bought for the twenty or so who remained. Ricky bought his own.

"Do you always get paid like this?" Ricky asked one of the other salesmen.

The man shrugged. "It depends. Last week it was chocolates...the week before, money. Not very much, though." He took a sip of his drink. "The week before *that* I got a cat."

"A cat?"

"Yeah. Top salesman."

"A live cat?" Ricky asked, glancing down at the turkey.

"Of course. What would I want with a dead cat?"

"What did everyone else get?"

"I can't remember."

Ricky was amazed that he could not remember. Another thought struck him.

"Did you get *one* turkey today?"

"Yeah."

"So did I."

"So?"

"But you've been there all week. I only started today."

"Thought I hadn't seen you before."

"So I'm paid five times as much as you," Ricky said, determined to thrash the matter out.

"I suppose you are." The man didn't seem very interested.

"What's the most you've ever earned?"

"What, in one week?"

"Yes."

The man considered the question. "Got to be the cat," he said.

"The most you've ever been paid is a *cat*?"

"It was a pedigree. Called a Maine Coon. Huge great thing, like a small leopard. I got seven hundred for it, no questions asked."

"Who would want to ask questions?"

"Well – taxman, RSPCA, local council..."

"Who did you sell it to?"

"A dealer."

"What did he do with it?"

"Now I come to think about it that he sold it back to us. I know Kasim shifted half a dozen Maine Coons to Tunisia last Thursday or Friday. Yeah, Friday, because it was the day I got the chocolates." He grimaced. "That wasn't a good week."

"It certainly wasn't a good week for the cat."

"In fact, I think they cancelled."

Like the cat, the conversation was going round in circles. Ricky drifted away. He bought another drink with the last of his change but, as he was paying, discovered a rolled up twenty pound note wedged in the bottom of his wallet. He decided to get drunk.

"Come on, turkey," he said to his wages, "we're going to tie a few on." The turkey said nothing.

Two hours later there were still about a dozen of them left in the pub, including Kasim who was negotiating the sale of the pig with Graham, the landlord. The carcass had been hoisted onto the bar and Graham was prodding its icy flanks, from time to time making tut-tut noises, like a metric plumber confronted with an imperial piece of piping.

"I don't know – turkeys, no problem, but this chappie...well, no demand, you see. Christmas, people want a turkey. It's natural."

Three people walked into the pub, took one look at the bar and walked out again. Ricky didn't blame them. Viewed from a certain angle the animal looked like a corpse.

"Tell you what, Kas," Graham said at last, "I'll give you fifty."

"Come on, it's worth twice that!"

The pub cat jumped onto the bar and delicately sniffed the pig's flank, twitching its nose in disbelief.

"I'd get out of here, cat," Ricky said, "you'll end up as the change." The cat turned to stare at him with green eyes as remote as planets.

"I can't do better than that. But, look, can you get me any more lampshades? I can shift them." Graham and two of the salesmen withdrew into a huddle.

The pig was once again propped up against the hat-stand and more drinks were ordered. The Maine Coon man paid for his with four pork chops, a unit of currency the barmaid accepted without comment. For a mad moment Ricky thought she was going to put them in the till.

"The economy of the country has collapsed," he told the turkey. "We're living in the Third World." He tried to slide his hand inside it, as if it were a ventriloquist's dummy. He noticed that people were staring at him.

"Marvo and his Amazing Talking Turkey," he explained.

"You could get a few drinks with that," one of the salesmen said.

"No way," Ricky said, "this turkey's coming home with me. I'm going to screw it to the wall as a trophy of my day's work."

"Going to screw it, more likely," the office wag suggested. "You've got your hand up its arse already."

This was true: to make it worse, he couldn't seem to get it out again. A piece of the ribcage was caught on his watchstrap. Ricky quietly wrestled with the animal's innards as hideous giblet juices began to leak down his arm.

"Time for a curry," the Maine Coon man suggested. Soon they were all outside, shivering in the frosty air. The pig was slung across two people's shoulders, and they set off for the Indian restaurant a hundred yards away, singing Christmas carols at the top of their voices. Ricky continued attempts to free his hand but his signet ring had now also got stuck. As they neared the restaurant, the social implications of the problem struck him. Even assuming they were prepared to serve a man with a turkey stuck on the end of his arm, it was not going to be easy to eat the meal. There was also the question of frostbite to consider.

"Let's see if Abdul wants the pig," someone said.

"He's not called Abdul!"

"Who cares? *Sell the man the pig!*"

"Sell the man the pig!" Everyone joined in the chant as they pushed open the door of the Star of India.

The idea that the restaurant might buy partially-thawed meat from Goldswan employees gave Ricky another reason to stick to poppadoms and lager, always assuming they got as far as ordering. He had passed the restaurant at lunchtime and had already marked it down as a place where you could get a two-course meal and the next ten days off work with amoebic dysentery, all for £8.99.

"Please prepare a table for fifteen," the Maine Coon man said in mock heroic tones. "We are prepared to submit this premium Staffordshire porker, killed only hours ago, in part settlement of our account." The pig was produced, held aloft like a ceremonial object at a coronation. "In addition, we can offer a selection of seasonal

carols to delight your other guests as they...as they dine...as they..."
It all rather started to fall apart at this point. "...as they eat here," he
finished lamely.

Ricky, who was near the front of the throng, peered drunkenly
through the gloom at the diners. All were staring at the intruders
with a mixture of terror and amusement.

The manager stepped forward. "Please get out," he said quietly.

The wag put his hand up. "Have you tried bacon curry? It'll be a
winner, with Christmas coming up."

The man's nerve snapped. "Get bloody out of my restaurant!" he
screamed.

There was a jostling from behind him which caused Ricky to lose
his balance. Without thinking he put out his left hand to steady
himself against a pillar. The turkey slipped effortlessly away from
the smooth surface: for a second he balanced precariously, his left
hand raised, his mind frantically trying to counterbalance the object
at the end of his arm. Then he was pushed again and he stumbled
forward. The turkey slammed down onto the edge of one of the
tables. A salver of Lamb Pasanda arced across the gangway and
slapped into the back of a man at the next table.

For a couple of seconds no one moved. Ricky looked down at the
carnage. Any attempt to explain the thing away as an accident was
out of the question.

"*Now* will you buy the pig?" the wag said.

"Right you bloody bastard fools," the manager shouted, rushing
towards the back of the restaurant. A few seconds later he returned
with three other men armed with baseball bats. Two of them made
for Ricky. Instinctively he put up his left arm to ward off the blow,
which landed across the turkey's backside. The reverberations went
up his arm and down his spine. It was like being plugged into the
mains. His attacker dropped the bat, ringing his hands. He looked
fearfully at the turkey, which he couldn't possibly yet have correctly

identified, as if it were endowed with preternatural powers.

The other blow, about three seconds later, caught Ricky on the nose and flung him back into the crowd. He could feel the blood pouring down his face, could taste its metallic, sobering tang in his mouth. Both sides used this opportunity to regroup.

Once again the Indians advanced but the salesmen had had enough. With a collective bellow they were out of the restaurant and down the street, Ricky half dragged by the Maine Coone man. The Indians followed to the corner, hurling fearful imprecations in several languages. After a hundred yards or they slowed, panting like wild animals.

"That was fun," the wag asked. Ricky mumbled, then threw up.

"Seemed like a nice restaurant," someone was saying.

"What you need," the wag went on, "is a taxi. Come on, on your feet." Ricky was beoming aware of his left hand, which was now throbbing badly. The blow from the Indian's baseball bat had forced his fingers right through the bird's spine. He was now welded so firmly to it that only a chain-saw or a controlled explosion seemed likely ever to separate them. He threw up again.

Somehow they found Ricky a cab; somehow the driver agreed to take him home; somehow he paid. A few flurries of snow whipped around his ankles as he stood on his doorstep, looking for his keys. Then he realised he had no keys. His keys were in the pocket of his coat and his coat was on the floor of the pub. He rang the bell.

After about twenty seconds the hall light was switched on, in the angry, abrupt way hall lights are switched on at eleven thirty at night. Then he saw Jane's outline, distorted by the frosted glass. Then the door opened and he saw Jane.

"Aaaghhhhh!" said Jane.

"I can explain everything," Ricky said thickly. He half stepped, half collapsed across the threshold.

"Jesus!" she shouted at him as he staggered into the front room.

"Here we go, another explanation!"

Ricky grinned wolfishly, as if at a compliment.

"Actually I don't want to know about the blood, or the sick or the chicken – or anything! *I don't want to know!*"

"Actually," Ricky said, "It's a turkey."

"Shut *up*! Listen, you layabout piss-head, I've had enough. You've got no money, you arse around all day long, you never...you never *do* anything! You never get anything *done!*"

Ricky was confused. Of all the many, many things she could have at that moment accused him of, 'not getting things done' was the most unexpected. "What sort of things?" he asked, really wanting to know.

"Everything! Nothing! For God's sake – look, it's over. Finished. Look at you – you've got a chicken stuck on the end of your arm. How can I have a conversation..."

"I've already said," Ricky said ponderously, "that it's a turkey. It's called Partridge," he added, stifling a giggle, "after the man who gave it to me. I was given a turkey by a partridge."

"What are you laughing at? What are you talking about anyway? God, you're a mess."

Ricky briefly sobered up. "Yes," he said abjectly. Everything was going wrong. If he was going to be able to laugh about all this tomorrow – not that he thought he would be – then he might as well laugh about it today. In fact, if he wasn't going to laugh about it tomorrow all the more reason to do so now. Suddenly he couldn't think of anything to laugh about. Yes, it was true. She was right. He was a mess.

"What a day," he said at last, as if that explained and excused everything. There was a long pause during which Ricky's mind more or less stopped working.

"I'm out of here," Jane said.

Ricky nodded to himself. This was more like it, this was the kind of conversation he had, for weeks, been expecting. It would have been easier, without the vomit and the blood and the broken nose – and the turkey, of course – to have carried it off with dignity but these things happen when they happen. He nodded again, this time more philosophically.

"Are you listening?" Jane asked, peering down at him. Somehow he seemed to have slid down onto the floor. He thought he'd stay there for a bit.

"Oh, yes," he said, trying to sound cool. "You're leaving me."

"Good. Well done."

"Is there someone else?" He had a vague idea that this was the sort of question people asked in these situations.

Jane reddened slightly. "There is, actually. But..."

"So," Ricky carried on relentlessly, "this hasn't got anything to do with my 'not getting things done'?"

"I don't want to talk about it." Tight-lipped, she walked round the living room, putting objects into a carrier bag apparently at random.

"That's the remote control. Are you going to fit the TV in that bag as well?"

She threw it at him. "I'll get the rest of my stuff at the week-end."

"Who is this hunk, anyway?"

"You wouldn't know him."

"You'd be surprised. I've met a lot of people recently."

"He's called Johann," she mumbled.

"What kind of a name is that?"

"South African."

"He's not in the footware game, is he?" Ricky asked, reaching for a bottle of whisky.

"What are you talking about?"

"I nearly sold some cat baskets to him today. If it was the same bloke." He unscrewed the bottle and took a long swig. "Probably wasn't, though."

"Don't you think you've had enough to drink?" Jane asked.

Ricky considered this. "No," he said.

Jane opened her mouth to speak but the right phrase eluded her.

"You going to ask about the turkey, aren't you?" Ricky said. "Go on, you can't resist it. Ask about the turkey."

"Sod you!" she shouted and marched out of the room, slamming the door behind her. About a minute later she did the same to the front door. Ricky heard her starting her car, crashing the gears and screeching away down the street. He looked down at the turkey.

"What a day," he said again. The turkey seemed to shift a little, but made no reply.

"Come on, me old mate," he said, lurching into the kitchen, "time we went to beddy-byes." He reached into a drawer and found an electric carving knife, then tested the blade against the turkey's back. It split the cellophane, but made no mark on the flesh. He went back into the living room where he took another long gulp of whisky. The room spun around for a moment: when he came to he was collapsed in the armchair. The wound on his face had reopened. Blood was dripping onto the carpet.

"Looks like it's just you and me for Christmas," he said to the turkey. "What a time we're going to have." Deep within the carcass of the beast, he felt something stirring, answering the probing caresses of his frozen fingers.

The Reflective Instruments Inspector

MARTHA HAD HER son David and her grandchildren to stay. The children were quiet and well-behaved. Sometimes it was hard to believe there was anyone in the house at all.

On Thursday, David was away to see about a job. By the time breakfast was over it was raining so the children accepted without complaint that they would have to play indoors. They made little noise but fiercely communicated their imagination to each other. The room was the bridge of a galleon flying in the teeth of a storm. Pirates were boarding; cannons roared and swords flashed in the starlight. Martha gripped the arms of her chair and watched the children play.

There was a knock on the front door and the fantasy billowed gently down to earth. Only a bowl of cherries on the table, a chest of heaped rubies, was unaltered by the intrusion.

"Morning," the man said. "Mrs Martha Janus?"

"Yes."

"Excellent. I'm the Reflective Instruments Inspector, from the Council. " He proffered a card. Martha looked at it quickly. The man stepped inside and consulted a clipboard. "Nasty day."

"Yes." There was a slightly awkward pause.

"So...I've got it here you have six reflective instruments on the premises. Is that right?"

"Er...yes, six...I think so, yes."

"Could we start in the bedroom?" They went upstairs and stood at the full-length mirror on the wardrobe door. The man produced a strange-looking torch which he shone onto the glass. Out of the corner of her eye, Martha saw the reflection of a woman moving across the landing.

"Friend, was it?" The man switched the torch off and produced a notebook. His pen hovered, waiting for her reply.

"I live alone," Martha heard herself saying. "I often think of my daughter. But that's not really her."

"I'll call it 'unknown.'"

"Thank you."

The man smiled encouragingly. They went into the bathroom and stared at the mirror there. The man got some calipers out of his bag and measured first Martha's face, then its reflection.

"I try to keep them true," Martha said, "after last time."

By way of reply, the man pointed at the spotless corner of wall and ceiling; then at its reflection, where a cobweb hung like a pale net.

"It's hard to keep *everything* up-to-date," Martha said.

"Have to make a note of it, though."

Martha reached inside the mirror and flicked at the cobweb. It folded itself up and fluttered down, out of the mirror, out of sight.

"So – third bedroom." He cocked his eye. "Nothing in the second?"

"No...the children – I thought it best not."

"Very wise." Once in the third bedroom, the man examined the surface of the mirror. He tapped it several times and held his hand up showing four fingers. Four fingers reflected back.

"No problems there," he said, making a further tick. "So...ah yes – hall." They went downstairs. A large mirror hung opposite the door. Tiny specks of corrosion billowed on the surface like woodworm.

From his bag the man produced a third object which he set up on the floor. The living room door opened and James and Mary took a couple of hesitant steps into the hall to stand next to their grandmother so that they were all reflected in the mirror. They watched the man carefully.

"What are you doing?" Mary said.

"Ha ha, well," the man said, making a final adjustment. "Now then..." He switched on the machine.

At first, the reflection didn't change. Then the images began to shift. Soon they were looking at something quite different. They were on the deck of a ship, storm-spray seeming to whip against their faces. A sail cracked. The flash of gunfire was all around them.

The children yawned and went back into the living room.

The man switched off his machine. Slowly the reflection returned to normal, just Martha standing in the hall and him bending over the instrument, straightening up, opening his mouth to speak.

"It's the children, that is," he said. "Your mirrors aren't licensed for children. You've got to apply. Their imagination throws your images every which way."

"I'll remember next time," Martha said humbly.

"How long are they here for?"

"I don't know. Perhaps a week."

The man made a note. "Okey-doke. Then we've got, let's see... 'powder compact – personal.'"

Martha fished the object out of her handbag. He glanced at it quickly and handed it back.

"Fine. Not much goes wrong with them, unless you leave them open."

"Oh, no. I've been warned."

"You never know what they'll pick up then. Particularly with the...you know, the children."

"Yes. It was in the leaflet."

"That's it, I think..." He scanned down his list. "Oh, hold up. 'Dressing table, main bedroom,' I've got here."

Martha's heart sank. Back they went upstairs. On her dressing table sat an old-fashioned mirror on a stand. The man examined it.

"Sit down, please," he said. He moved to lean over her shoulder. Their faces were pressed close, like lovers. Martha saw the image of her face slowly smoothing, the lines fading, the hair thickening, falling about her shoulders. Soon she was looking at a reflection, familiar in that mirror, of a woman half her age. The piercing eyes of the man in the glass made her face drop in shame.

"Madam," he said gently but firmly. She looked back at the mirror. Gradually the image stabilised.

"Your age is, let's see…"

"Sixty eight."

"Sixty eight. That reflection was no more than thirty? Forty?" He looked at her kindly. "Say forty. The fines are banded, you see."

"I know."

The man sat down on the edge of the bed and started to fill in a form on his tablet, making reference to his earlier notes.

"You've been in trouble twice before. There *have* been some improvements – third bedroom, for instance, and the bathroom, except for that cobweb – but the others are serious. Self-flattery – that's this. Third offence, too. And Unlicensed Juvenile Imagination… one 'Unknown Person'…one 'False Housework'." He turned to his price sheet. "Self-flat…UJI…UP…and a False." He totalled the figures and waited; presently a piece of paper chattered quietly out the back of the tablet. He tore it off and handed it to Martha. "A hundred and eighteen pounds this time, Mrs Janus. Most of that's for the UJI, in the hall. I've got to charge for a week's child licence as well."

He stood up and adopted a formal tone.

"I have to warn you that, this being your third offence, you'll be receiving another inspection without notice in the next seven days. Any irregularities will result in your Mirror Licence being revoked, which will mean all reflective instruments will have to be removed from the premises. You may also be required to attend a hearing before the Mirrors Board." There was a pause.

"Do I pay you?" she asked.

"Oh no, madam, I'm not allowed to take money. You pay the Council. The details are on the form."

Martha tried to remember the days before mirrors had been revealed to be so multi-faceted, before they had been licensed by the council and before these fearful machines detected every nuance of self-examination. So much had changed in the ten years since 2016 when the council's cuts had really started to bite. She suspected more changes would follow.

As if reading her thoughts – which, indeed, he had been trained to do – the man pointed to the bottom of the form. "You can also go to this link to see the consultation document for IDM."

"For what"

"Imagination, Dreams and Memories."

"I hadn't heard about that."

The man smiled thinly. "It's been on the website for months."

Martha said nothing. It was now expected that the citizens should be constantly online to apprise themselves of the council's latest schemes. This wasn't obligatory but no concession was made to those who were ignorant as a result.

"Yes, they'll be licensed from next March."

Martha felt her head swimming. A faint flicker of revolt stirred inside her. "So if I want to object, I can," she said.

The man looked at her pityingly. "Well, in theory, yes. But..." He gave a light laugh. "Makes no difference. One way or another, it's going to happen."

"Than what's the point of the consultation?"

"It's the law," he said severely. Martha was briefly shocked, as if she had been caught red-handed at a crime scene.

"I suppose it's all for the best," she said humbly. After all, the council had to get money from somewhere to pay for the children's centres, play groups, libraries, busses and so on. Not that there were many of these things; although there were plenty of inspectors and compliance officers with their terrible machines like the one that the man was now holding in his hand. In a vague way, she realised that life only creates similar versions of itself. Inspectors tended to produce more inspectors, not more libraries. Again she stifled the rebellious thought. What was the point? Everything was justified by the need to raise money. That's what they were told. The evils and privations were only temporary. Even now, great plans were being worked on for the betterment of life: and one fine day...

"Anyway," he said, "must crack on. Six more calls this morning."

They went downstairs. Martha opened the front door. He turned to face her and re-assumed his official voice. "Do try to do better, Mrs Janus," he said as he stepped outside. "This doesn't give me any pleasure, you know. It's regulations. The same for everyone."

Martha went back to the living room. The children were at the controls of a plane. All the engines were ablaze and the plane was dropping out of the sky like a winged bird. Only by extraordinary presence of mind were they able to control it, bring it in to land. Martha smiled and sat down.

"Grrrooaaahhh!" James said. James was a lion.

When David came back at six the children were quietly watching television. They greeted him politely, their minds on other worlds.

"What have you two been doing? Watching the idiot box?" He turned to his mother with a smile. "Kids nowadays haven't any imagination. Imagination costs nothing. Without imagination, where are your dreams?" He flung out his hand dramatically, as though he still had a dream so close it could almost be touched. The moment passed and his briefly animated expression turned into a yawn. The children stared at him uncomprehendingly, awash with dreams and imagination that swamped the grey reality in which the adults were forced to live. David stared back, then pointed at the television. "Spend all day looking at their reflections."

"Yes, dear," she said. Then she got up and went into the kitchen to put the dinner on.

The Wrong Door

THE VILLAGE IS called Southelton. County: Suffolk. Population: 442. Pubs: two, The Old Bell and The Fox. Distance from sea: between three and three and a half miles depending on if the tide is in or out. One Post Office, one bookshop, one shop where you can buy stuff like string and lager and biros and baked beans and organic mushrooms. No station, no doctor, no butcher, no baker, no candlestick-maker. You get the idea. The name, as I said, is Southelton but don't ask me how it's pronounced. I've heard half a dozen different versions, including two from the same person, since we moved here.

Actually, that's not quite true. The last bit. We haven't 'moved' here, in the sense that we have no other residence. There's the house in London which, if we're honest, is where the real stuff is. So, yes, let's use the word: we're weekenders.

No, we're not. We *do* come down most weekends (though it's a bitch of a drive and even worse on the train) but either Emma or I or both of us are sometimes here for longer. On Monday as well, for instance. Or Thursday. See what I mean? And you can guarantee that, if we *are* down of a weekday, we make sure we buy some string, or a stamp, or a book, or some mushrooms, even if we don't really need them, just to prove we're present out of hours.

Look – I don't want to make a big thing about this. It's just that some others do. In any community there's stuff that goes on and we want to be involved. We're both sociable. We care about where we happen to be. We're interested in other people. We have to be: Emma's a journalist and I'm a screenwriter.

Now I'm making it worse. I can see what you're thinking and it's the same as some people must be thinking here. I know someone local could have bought this house, instead of which they're living with their parents in Thruxbridge or Ashfield Green. That's not our fault. I can look myself in the mirror and can say that we've met the situation more than half-way. Emma managed to get a piece about the bookshop into a national which resulted in a spike in visitors for several months. I've been asked to join the parish council which would be great except the meetings are on Wednesdays. We buy raffle tickets and paperbacks and pints of beer. We have our weekend papers delivered by the local firm. All we want to do is keep our noses clean, play the game, fit in. Who doesn't?

These good intentions have been on the go for six years now and I was beginning to think that we were getting somewhere, were starting to mould our lives around the local human landscape. Then, last Saturday, the whole thing seemed to explode in our faces.

It started when I decided to have a birthday party. No, I'm not going to tell you which one. Our house is quite open-plan and can, with some re-organisation, accommodate about 50 sitting down. So, that was the number we went for.

The next decision we took was to order everything locally. Wine, beer, meat, veg, fish, bread, glasses, trestle tables, chairs, cutlery and catering help could all be sourced from within a six-mile radius so we did that. See what I mean – we were plugged in, aware, keen to do the right thing.

The guest list. I'm however-old-I-am and I know a few people. Emma ditto. Two different but parallel careers and with friendships that stretched back to the 19-whatevers. It was *my* birthday so my friends counted more than hers. Even so.

Cut a long story short, our 'must have' list, when totted up, came to about 90 people. So, start again. Past disagreements or suspicions of unsuitability intruded, perhaps to the detriment of our future relationship with these people – not only had their slight failings now been aired between us but there was the fear that, some of them being known to the guests, the news would leak out and feathers would be ruffled. So, we'd need an embargo, a radio-silence, a complete news lockdown imposed on the invitees. We'd done this before, professionally, but not socially. We could deal with that.

We then realised this winnowed list left no room for any of our newer Southelton friends. Most of the rooms at the pubs and the B&Bs would be booked by the guests so any local secrecy was impossible. Would people talk? How would they judge us? What should we do?

Suddenly, it all seemed too much. Should we have the party in London? Or no party at all, just go to Provence for a long weekend and eat and drink ourselves stupid in Valbonne or on the Croisette?

I was poised at the phone to cancel the orders and call the whole thing off when Emma pointed out that we were being ridiculously solipsistic. No one gave a damn what anyone else did any more. The people who lived round here had already decided what they thought of us and one party wasn't going to change that. Publish and be damned, in other words. So, out went the invites.

Now we dolly back, fade to black and bring the lights back up on the scene at about 1.30am on the night of the party. From now on you need to pay quite close attention. Were I to have done so, this disaster might have been averted.

So, we had Sean, Toby and Rachel doing the catering and the serving. For reasons not made clear at the time of booking, all were dressed in elaborate and, as later became clear, expensive Pierrot costumes. This certainly cut a dash during the event. Toby and Rachel had left already: Sean, however, was doing another job in the area the following day so it had seemed easiest for us to put him up in a local B&B. At or shortly after 1.30am, I therefore walked Sean down the road, round the corner and up the hill to the B&B as he wasn't sure where it was and I wasn't sure I could describe it.

I'd been there earlier that day to pick up the key but, as events were to prove, had been too frazzled to take in all the details. Mary, the owner, had explained it all carefully: the lock turns like *this* – his room is upstairs, on the *right*. The bathroom is *here*. Blah blah blah. I was worrying about other things, like whether we should have put Richard and Jane on the same table, who was meeting Mike off the train and if we had enough beer. As I left she mentioned that Bobo, as he was known, who ran the local garage, lived next door. That set me thinking about MOTs: another irrelevant distraction. I vaguely noticed that the two houses were effectively two semis which had originally been four cottages. I wish now I'd paid more attention to one important aspect of them.

As it happened, one of the boxes of wine glasses hadn't been used. Sean's job the next day required these so it seemed easiest to take them with us. Off we went in the dark, the large rugby-playing Sean still in his silk Pierrot costume, me carrying the box of glasses – down the road, round the corner and up the hill, like I said. I wasn't entirely sober. Did I mention this? Did you infer it? It's impossible to pretend that this didn't have some bearing on what was about to happen.

We got to the house and walked up the short drive where a large car was parked. I put the key in the lock and turned it. Nothing happened. Tried again but no dice. Tried the other way round but it wouldn't go in at all. Had I picked up the wrong key? It was a Yale, millions like it, perhaps half a dozen on our house. It had a loop of string round it. Our shed key had string as well. Perhaps string bought from the same shop. I squinted at it, then tried again, this time with the string looped around my left wrist. Result as before.

Then I noticed that the window immediately to the right of the door was unbolted. If I opened it and reached in, I might – or so my deranged logic ran – be able to open the door from the inside. Still with my other hand holding the key I pushed the window open and reached my right arm inside.

Whatever grabbed me must have been very well trained because there was no warning and no noise, merely an agonising pain as what felt like half a dozen steak knives clamped down on my wrist. Then I felt a lateral shaking movement that suggested either a shark or a dog. Probably, in the circumstances, a dog: but a bloody big one as my hand was about four feet above the ground. My head and shoulders were partly pulled in through the window. The pane seemed about to give way.

I don't know what Sean thought was happening. With my other hand still looped around the string attached to the key in the lock, it might have seemed as if I was, inexplicably, trying to embrace the door frame. The unseen jaws clamped down harder. I probably screamed, as would you have done.

At that point things started happening very quickly.

Thundering footsteps down the stairs, the front door flung open, breaking the string and snapping off the Yale key in the lock. The window swung inwards and the pane smashed. The dog released its grip. I staggered back against the wall. A man, dressed only in boxer shorts, charged out. The outside light came on, casting me into shadow and illuminating Sean in his Pierrot costume, standing on the drive next to the Range Rover, the box of wine glasses on the ground. The man bore down on him.

Sean, as I said, was a rugby player so his reaction was instinctive. He threw himself forward and took the man round the ankles. Both crashed to the ground: first, with a noise like 24 simultaneous Jewish weddings, against the box of wine glasses; then, with a noise like a dull drum roll, against the passenger door of the Range Rover. All its lights came on, as did the car's strident alarm.

I realised that the man who had rushed out of the house, and whose red boxer shorts were now round his ankles, was Bobo the garage owner.

At this point, I was also aware of a darkly-dressed figure running up the drive towards the car.

The dog, which looked like a cross between a pit bull and a bear, came hurtling out the door like a guided missile. It ignored its master, naked and semi-conscious by the car, and fastened its attention on the only moving object in its line of sight. When still six feet away it took off and flung itself towards the newcomer's throat.

I was able to see that the newcomer was a priest – or, at least, was dressed in priest's clothes – because at this point another light, this time in the hall, was switched on and a tall and dramatic-looking woman with a tangled mane of dark hair appeared in the doorway. She was wearing a long crimson dressing gown and had a carving knife in her hand. She was closely followed by a girl of about six.

The dog had missed its intended target but had fastened itself on the cleric's shoulder. He screamed. Both collapsed into the hedge by the driveway. The girl let out a yell that was even louder, more piercing and more insistent than the car alarm.

The woman advanced towards Sean, brandishing the knife in his face. There was something of a crazed high priestess about her, or an Amazonian queen on the eve of battle. The child was still screaming and had now been joined by another one, also screaming: and by two much smaller dogs which, from behind the children, set off a series of staccato barks.

Sean and Bobo were wrestling on the half-mud, half-gravel of the drive. Like in a Western, each time one tried to straighten up and explain, the other would fell him with a hefty blow. Due to the broken glass from the box, and perhaps the unforgiving gravel on the drive, Sean's Pierrot costume was shredded and Bobo's buttocks and back were scourged as if by a flagellant's whip.

I was beyond imagining what anyone else in the village might have thought what was going on. I was to hear several interpretations in the days and weeks that followed.

I couldn't cower in the shadow of the house for ever. The whole situation was slipping dangerously towards a full-scale brawl but, even if I made everything worse, I had to do *something*. I moved towards Bobo and Sean and tried to pull them apart. The woman, seeing yet another intruder, swung round to face me, knife raised. The children's screaming re-doubled.

She started to shout something – it was impossible to make out more than the odd word over the general din – and would, I think, have struck out: but just then I was caught a glancing and perhaps accidental blow by the naked Bobo which made me lose my footing and topple into the hedge. To my right I could hear the dog and the priest still struggling in the nearby undergrowth. My foot had got snarled round a tree root so that, when I finally emerged, it was minus a shoe and with a torn trouser leg.

The scene was much as before: Sean and Bobo were still rolling on the ground; but the woman, still with the knife in one hand, was now trying to bash Sean over the head with a dustbin lid.

Then yet another light, brighter than all the others, came on from the building next door. The front door opened and a middle-aged woman stepped onto the threshold. She had a torch in her hand and flashed it around. I recognised her as Mary.

There were three main tableaux for her to consider. A priest fighting with a dog in the shrubbery; a naked man, a harlequin and a Boudica-like woman grappling on the drive; and a terrified posse of howling children and yelping dogs in the doorway.

There was also, standing on the edge of the action, a tousle-haired raggedy man with torn clothes, a bleeding hand and one shoe, a kind of ineffectual and bemused everyman/observer. Each group was symbolic of something or other: viewed *in toto,* however, the scene acquired a vast but obscure allegorical significance which in many ways possessed all the thematic and compositional attributes of great art.

Without warning the car alarm petered out into a faint burble, followed by silence.

"What on *earth* is going on?" Mary asked.

Everyone – even the clerical newcomer and the dog – stopped what they were doing and turned to face her. For a long moment, nothing was said. It was as if everyone had been suddenly called to their senses.

Now that the scene was fully illuminated, I saw the cause of my mistake. The two houses were not, as is more common with pairs of properties, mirror images of each other but exact facsimiles, with the small window being on both cases to the right of the door. I'd tried to go into the first rather than the second. I started babbling about this to Mary: but the scene in front of her could not be so easily explained.

Something about the change of key must have communicated itself because suddenly everyone became all loved-up. Mary embraced the Vicar – who had, it transpired, been passing on his way back from some late-night act of corporeal charity and selflessly intervened in what he thought was a burglary. The woman, Bobo's wife, embraced Sean, whom she knew slightly. Bobo, still naked, embraced his dog. The two small children embraced each other. No one embraced me: but then, I didn't deserve an embrace. I stood in the middle of all this, a stranger at my own catastrophe, blood still seeping from my right wrist.

Mary came up to me and I explained again, this time more lucidly, what had happened and how I'd got confused and gone for the wrong house.

"You won't make that mistake again, will you?" she asked.

I thought of the damage: her key; Bobo's lock; Bobo's window; Bobo's car door; 24 wine glasses; Sean's Pierrot costume; the priest's cassock; my suit trousers; my shoe; my reputation.

"No," I said. "I won't."

In fact, and despite what I said earlier, I needn't have worried about the last one. From then on, I was a made man. I had caused the best single incident in Southelton since Old Jack Beacham had drunkenly crashed his tractor into the Police Station after the '73 village fête. Everywhere I went for the next few months I was, with friendly rolls of the eyes or backslapping bonhomie, invited to give my version of events. I'd arrived.

I told the story often but, with a screenwriter's eye, carefully edited it each time. I noted each reaction to different parts of the tale which, the next time, made me emphasise one point in favour of another, conflate two moments or omit altogether aspects that seemed to be of less dramatic value.

What I'm trying to say is that you shouldn't trust this version as being accurate. You're welcome to ask any of the others but, being more viscerally involved, I doubt they'd be more objective. What *is* truth, anyway? I'll tell you – it's anything that you want to believe. So, unless another version of this event comes along that you prefer, then you're stuck with mine. It's now yours to pass on as you wish. Or to change if you want to. After all, *I* did.

Nine Grand

"THE PROBLEM IS," Pete said, "he hasn't got any money."

Carol gave him a level stare. "What are you proposing to do about it?"

They'd talked around the question for some time. Knowing her husband as she did, Carol could see what was coming.

"It's a question of nine grand. That's what he needs. But he wouldn't accept it from me."

She was about to ask why it was important that Pete bail Rickie out but she knew the answer. They'd been friends since way back and Pete had, frankly, had all the luck. They both had talent – Rickie for making art and Pete for making money – and it was the luck that was, now as ever, causing the guilt.

Pete had made two small piles, from publishing and from IT. Most recently, his account had been swelled by the death of his father, whom he'd never greatly liked, whose will had been proved at the surprisingly large sum of £800,000. Pete suspected that the fact his wealth had been concealed suggested something dubious about how it had been made. Pete's father had been a lawyer working in and around the fringes of the city, which supported this view.

Rickie, on the other hand, had been dogged by ill-fortune. When he was six he'd lost half his thumb in a car accident. His parents had been well meaning but inept and had been swindled out of their savings in a time-share scam. Rickie's life as an artist, a perilous enough calling at the best of times, had staggered from one crisis to another. A rich benefactor had died the day before a meeting which would have confirmed a massive commission. His aunt, from whom Rickie nurtured expectations, had late in life married her secretary who scooped the pot when she died in a boating accident in Spain. Two months ago, his studio in Bethnal Green had been destroyed in a fire. The contents included virtually everything of any worth Rickie had created.

The final and current irony was that he'd been awarded a place to study at the RCA from September. It was now late August. He had no art and, worst of all, no money. Cash needed to be found quickly. It was only that morning that Pete had realised how precarious his friend's situation was.

Rickie still had his pride, or at least Pete thought so. Certainly the question of their increasing disparity of wealth had remained unspoken between them for 20 years. It could not be spoken of now.

Carol studied her husband. He was a good man. He wore his wealth and his good fortune lightly. More than once she had spotted small acts of generosity to friends, Rickie included: the falsely low restaurant bill agreed with the owner, the balance settled by Pete privately; the supposedly free theatre tickets which Pete had in fact paid for; the purchase of an artwork of Rickie's through a proxy. Carol had always rather liked the piece, a sinister but elegant abstract creation in variety of pale metals which called to mind a necklace, and a strange flower, and an escaped spirit, all housed in a glass bell-jar which perfectly conveyed the idea that the work was part of some long-forgotten and esoteric Victorian collection. In case Rickie saw it and twigged, it had to be kept out of sight.

Pete had never broadcast these acts of generosity, even to Carol – she had discovered some and suspected others – which made them all the more genuine. It was for this reason, and others, that she still loved him; and was therefore happy to tolerate, even indulge, his generosity. It was his money after all. She also had her own. For this reason too they were comfortable together.

The Rickie situation could not, however, be remedied by small gestures. Fairly serious money was needed. Pete was pacing up and down. He went to the fridge, opened a bottle of Chablis, poured two glasses and sat down opposite her. She knew what this meant. They were now in conference and he was going to thrash the matter out.

"You could get the money to him anonymously," she said. "There must be a dozen ways."

Pete took a sip of wine. "Name two."

"Well…you could tell him he'd won a prize…"

"No one falls for that any more. Anyway, he's suspicious. Plus, you'd need a bank account under a fictitious name to pay him from. That might have been easy to set up twenty years ago. Not now."

"You could transfer the money to his account."

"He'd know where it came from."

"It could be a mistake. By the bank."

"How could I tell him that? Anyway, he's honest. And nervous about money." Pete filled up the glasses. "The trouble is, he doesn't understand it. When he has it, he thinks he doesn't deserve it and doesn't know what to do with it. When he doesn't have it, he doesn't know how to get it."

"How about buying one of his artworks – oh, forget that. They've all been burnt. Hey – you could commission him to do something and pay up front." She took a big slug of wine. "That's it."

Pete was shaking his head. "The art world doesn't work like that. Plus, if I were to commission something he would spent half the money on materials and half his time on making it when he should be studying. He's very diligent, wouldn't want to rip me off."

It seemed to Carol that each of Rickie's many virtues presented real obstacles to his happiness, but said nothing.

The wine was finished before they agreed that there was only one way, in this particular time and with this particular person, of getting nine grand anonymously to a struggling artist.

* * *

Pete was broadly right in his assessment of Rickie's situation and character but with one important error. Pete's opinion of Rickie's attitude to wealth was predicated on this being the same as his own. For Pete, being poor was the worst thing he could imagine. Rickie had always been poor and viewed money with a mixture of misgiving and confusion. He had lived hand to mouth for so long that poverty was normal. He got by and was personable enough to have a decent circle of friends. He was, as Pete also knew, honest: and like Pete with his wealth, he wore this honesty lightly. He told a good story, was self-deprecating without being abject, dealt fairly with his lovers and his creditors. Add to this his sufficient talent and his absolute dedication and you had a man of integrity. So it was that he was able to survive where better artists, but lesser men, had failed to.

None the less, as Pete and Carol were finishing their Chablis, Rickie was sitting in his living room overlooking Colombia Road with his mind clouded and depressed to an extent he'd rarely known. There were three main problems, which between them infected every aspect of his thoughts.

The first was the loss of his studio. Any good artist, writer or composer always believes that their next creation will be the big one. None the less, the destruction of the best part of twenty years' work was hard to bear. Yes, there were photos: but were he to have been a novelist or a songwriter the question wouldn't have arisen, every sentence and every bar being saved to the cloud moments after it was created.

The second was the RCA course. This was a game-changer. To have been offered it at all vindicated everything he had tried to achieve: but he needed money, more immediately and in larger quantities, than at any time before. The rent here was already more than he could afford. A host of other costs were building up as well. He was aware of how many times Pete had arranged that the full cost of the kind of evening he had wanted to enjoy had fallen mainly on him. He knew that the pleasure of giving is greater than that of receiving, even though he had rarely been in the former situation.

As he stubbed out his roll-up he resolved to make a virtue out of necessity, call Pete and ask for help. It would be possible to dress it in a way which gave his friend – whose obsession with money and profit Rickie over-estimated – a benefit. He could, for instance, create a work of art for him. With an RCA degree at his back, this would be worth three times more than it would today. Pete was a good mate. Rickie would swallow his pride and call him tomorrow. But would he say yes?

The third problem, which was different from and yet trumped both of the first two, was what was going on at number 31 across the road. He knew a drug den when he saw it. As he tilted his head, he was looking at one. This caused him disquiet for several reasons. One, as many people would share, was the late-night noise, and at times the violence, which sometimes went beyond what one might fairly expect from a London street.

There was also a darker concern. More than once, since these troubles had started brewing, Rickie had needed the oblivion and disconnection that only powerful opiates can provide. Twice in the last month he had trafficked in products he could ill-afford and which left him with the sensation that he was on the top of a snow-capped and mist-ringed mountain, about to experience a transcending rush before crashing into the darkness below. Each time he had, with great difficulty, managed to engineer a kind of controlled landing. Much as he needed the highs he was all too aware of the lows. All this was due to something that most of his friends, including Pete, had never known or suspected: for, until about three years ago, Rickie had had a very nasty little heroin habit which was in serious danger of being re-kindled.

* * *

Rickie was out the next day and came back at dusk. The windows at the den across the road at number 23 were bathed in their usual crepuscular light, suggesting dark transactions in shadowy corners. People came and went with their usual furtive frequency.

The operation was run by a man called Will. He would have much preferred that business were conducted under a higher wattage where he could judge customers more clearly and where thefts or other deceptions would be more apparent. However, he'd had to accept that bright lights spooked his clients. Like Rickie, Will was honest. He paid suppliers on the nail and expected the same from his customers. If he said that coke was £35 a gram and a bag of smack £12, those were the prices. If he said he'd never deal with a supplier again after he'd sold Will something cut with rat poison, he never would. If he said he owed you a £100, he'd pay you. If he said he was going to break your arm, he'd break your arm. You knew where you stood with Will: and, in this shifting world, there was much to be said for that.

One thing that irritated him, the matter of the lighting aside, was that most of the transactions had to be done in cash. He would have preferred chip and pin, BACS or Bitcoins but his clients would never have been able to cope with these options. Most had little more than the cash they'd scraped together for the deal. Where they'd got this from was not Will's problem. His honesty and integrity had strict boundaries. He looked after his own business. How everyone else managed theirs was up to them – end of.

Cash had started to loom larger in Will's mind because, recently, seven grand that was owed to him had gone AWOL. He hadn't yet worked out who had ripped him off or screwed up. Perhaps Scotty and Asbo, two of his less-trusted henchmen; perhaps the problem was further down the line. He'd take his time and sort it out.

* * *

Rickie, who had gone out for some chips, walked up to his first-floor flat and opened the door. There was a thick envelope on the floor just below the letter box. He picked it up, went into the living room, turned on the light and took it over to the desk by the window that overlooked the street and, opposite it, Will's empire at number 23.

The envelope was flexible and over an inch thick. It was white and stout and sealed with tape but there was nothing written on it. He felt curiously reluctant to open it. He was expecting nothing of this nature, hand-delivered or otherwise.

Standing there with the light behind him and the curtains open and holding in his right hand something about the size of a gun or a wad of cash, Rickie was likely to attract attention: and he did.

Asbo in the first-floor room directly opposite was in a nervous, twitchy mood, waiting for a tricky customer to turn up who was, as always, late. This bloke across the road seemed to be staring at him. That wouldn't do. Asbo stood up to close the half-drawn curtains.

As he did so, something about the man's manner caught his attention. Furtively – partly out of necessity but mainly out of habit, for Asbo did everything furtively – he watched the man open the envelope, stare incredulously at its contents and remove them. Asbo saw they were banknotes, several wads of them, each bound with rubber bands. The light caught them and he could see they were purple. Twenties. Asbo was used to looking at money. He reckoned that lot was between seven and ten grand. He licked his lips.

After a pause, the man opened the desk drawer and put the notes in it. Then he turned away and picked up what might have been a coat. Jeez, he was going out – this was going to be easier than Asbo had dared hope. Two minutes later the man left the house and turned left down the road, deep in thought. Asbo grinned. When he came back he'd have something else to think about.

* * *

Rickie did indeed want to think. What the hell was going on? The money looked like about ten grand. There was no note. Where had it come from? What was it intended to buy? He'd forgotten that this was the kind of sum he urgently needed. He prided himself on his ability to concentrate utterly on whatever he was creating but ignored the flip side: that he was, when so engaged, incapable of recognising, still less thinking about, anything else. This may be a good recipe for artistic endeavour but it's a poor way of coping with life in a big city when threats, opportunities and decisions appear without warning, each clamouring for attention. So it was that he found himself constantly in the red; spending, for instance, so much time on perfecting a work of art that he ignored how much his materials were costing and failed to chase previous clients for money or lay effective groundwork for future commissions.

His current problem was the reverse. Bereft of both past creations and present inspiration, he was none the less rolling in cash. The provenance worried him. It was clear that the terms were uncertain. By accepting it, what would he be committing to?

He had thought about going to score some smack in Hackney but now realised that this was not an appropriate reaction. Also, he had no money on him. He laughed. What an irony. He turned and retraced his steps down Cambridge Heath Road.

* * *

Asbo acted swiftly. Telling Scotty that he had to go out for ten minutes and to deal with the client if he showed, he got some tools from the first-floor cupboard and slipped out of the house.

Just as Asbo had spied on Rickie, so the ever-suspicious Scotty now spied on Asbo. Scotty saw Asbo cross the road and go into number 22. A few minutes later he saw him in the front room. Those who forget the past are condemned to repeat it: and Asbo had not learned from Rickie's misfortune and didn't draw the curtains.

Scotty saw Asbo reach into the drawer, take the money, and leave the room. When Asbo got back to the house, Scotty was ready for him.

* * *

Asbo was an experienced burglar. As he had the advantages of knowing what he was looking for and where it was, when Rickie returned soon afterwards there was no evidence anyone had been in the flat. It was only when Rickie pulled open the drawer and saw no envelope there that his reason snapped.

Rickie knew when he was pissed or high and when he wasn't so he was certain the envelope had been there before he left. Now it wasn't. No one seemed to have been in the flat. He had been burgled before so knew what that looked like. His mind filled up with theories and then, like a blocked toilet, stopped working altogether.

He found himself back in the position he had been in half an hour before: standing, hopeless and confused, by the window and staring at number 23.

What was going on there was interesting. Two polices cars, sirens wailing, had turned up and four coppers were wrestling someone to the ground. Another person had run indoors and, after a scuffle, was hauled out. A police van turned up and the two men were flung into the back. The police stood about questioning people for a bit: then the convoy slipped away, sirens now stilled, in the direction of Bethnal Green nick.

Rickie couldn't tear his view away. There was some connection between the events that he could not see.

* * *

What had happened after Asbo's visit to Rickie's flat can be very simply told.

Scotty challenged Asbo to say what he had been up to. Asbo, spooked that he'd been watched, refused. Scotty reminded him of a favour Asbo owed him. Asbo refuted this. Scotty put out his arm. Asbo threw a punch. Scotty threw a punch. Asbo staggered back onto the pavement, blood streaming from his nose. Scotty followed him and grabbed him round the throat. Unnoticed, an envelope fell from Asbo's pocket and fell into the dank weeds by the wall in front of the house. A public-spirited passer-by dialled 999 and gave a succinct description of what was happening. Two patrol cars happened to be in the area and were there in minutes. The rest you know.

* * *

The key turned in the door and Pete came in. He was running his hands back and forth across his hair as if to check it was still there, his habit when he was stressed.

"Did you drop it off?" Carol asked.

"Yeah." he sat down then stood up again, looking slightly wildly round the room.

"All OK?"

"Sure." He sat down again. "I mean, it wasn't that hard. What could go wrong?"

Carol could think of several – as indeed could Pete – but merely gave a non-committal shrug. She poured him a glass of wine and, as she passed it to him, kissed his forehead. "You're a good man. A good friend."

For the first time since he'd come in, Pete smiled. He seemed reassured. "I think so," he said.

* * *

For Will, what had just happened had broken every rule. Although Asbo and Scotty were unreliable and had bad blood between them, both had useful qualities so Will had followed a policy of divide and rule. Now they'd both been carted off in a meat wagon, the punters had scattered and the police had something tangible. This might prove stronger than the blackmail he held over a Sergeant and a Detective Inspector at the local nick. With ABH involved, the thing could spiral out of control. Asbo and Scotty had quite possibly undone two years' work.

That problem was filed away for the morrow, when they would have been released and either flee or return shamefaced to number 23. What concerned him now was putting a lid on things. Will had seen more of what had gone on in the last hour than Asbo, Scotty or Rickie would ever know. It was clear that the argument had involved money. It was equally clear that the man across the road was involved. By an excusable association of ideas, Will saw a connection between this and the recent loss of cash.

There was no reason to delay. Will crossed the road, pushed open the front door, went upstairs and rang Rickie's bell. A few moments later Rickie appeared.

"Hi," Will said, "We need to talk." He gently ushered Rickie into the hall and shut the door behind him.

Rickie offered no resistance. He led the way into the living room and sat down. Will sat down opposite him.

For a while, Will said nothing. He was conducting a rapid survey of Rickie and of the room. The man was in some kind of creative profession, Will could tell that by his clothes. Basically of no fixed abode – the place didn't have the clutter or warmth that spoke of a home. Everything suggested a lack of money. The man was guilty and confused. He'd seen him before, had marked his twitchy manner and pegged him as an ex-junkie. He'd relapsed recently: he was hating, and also loving, the thing that once had been the centre of his soul. That he had relapsed suggested a stress or problem, which probably came back to money. This was a man who did not understand the stuff. No one who lived in a flat like this could.

All these thoughts and conclusions ran through his mind in about three seconds. For a while longer he sat still, saying nothing, staring across the room at the unhappy man opposite him, partly just because he could but mainly to be sure.

Not for the first time, Will wondered what he was doing in this game. His clear and immediate perceptions about a situation would have made him a millionaire in any reputable business, rather than a millionaire in an illegal one. Even now, with a crucial conversation about to happen, he afforded himself the time to reflect on this career and why he still pursued it. Was it the risk – or was it that, by being outside the law that most people respected, he could make himself the absolute master of the world he'd chosen to create?

Now, however, the clang of the prison door could be heard. These reflections, like the matter of Asbo and Scotty, were postponed. This man sitting opposite him was the centre of his troubles.

Will suddenly offered Rickie a smile. Rickie returned with a ghastly one of his own.

"I think you know who I am."

Rickie blinked. "No."

"I know who *you* are. I live across the road and I've got a problem." Rickie was about to ask what kind of problem this was but Will kept the initiative. "I've lost something. It may have been mis-delivered. People do make mistakes. Two of my associates, earlier, made a mistake as well. Two mistakes, in fact."

There was a long silence, during which Rickie struggled with various conflicting emotions. "I don't know what's happened," he said at last. His head sunk down.

"But you do know *something* about this. You can help me. And I can help you. I don't think anyone else can right now."

Rickie said nothing. He was in no position to help himself. Nor could he think what the right answers were: not that the man had actually asked anything, merely stated facts, which was far more unsettling. Indeed, Rickie could barely think at all.

Will realised this and stood up. No more could be accomplished tonight. He tossed a small plastic bag onto the table. "It's on me. You need it. We'll talk tomorrow."

Will had another of his intuitions. The man was just a dupe. Somehow he'd got involved in this by accident. There was a package involved. This bloke had just got mixed up in it. He didn't think he was any threat. He watched Rickie hungrily eye the bag on the table. Come tomorrow, the man would be either a client or an absentee. Asbo and Scotty were the ones he needed to deal with, unreliable bastards. Their time was up.

"See you tomorrow," he said with an airy wave, and left Rickie in a state of darkening confusion.

* * *

Next thing Rickie knew he was coming down. He felt as if he was falling through the sky and being tossed in a brutal thunderstorm, tumbling towards a dark and jagged landscape into which he knew he would soon crash. By the time this sensation had passed it was nearly four in the morning. On the floor by his side was a small bag to which a few small crystals still clung.

He rolled over and stared blankly through the undrawn curtains at number 23 across the road. From this position, he could only see the roof, orange in the streetlight and faintly sheened with what he realised was rain. He felt an itch in his left arm and reached to scratch it.

* * *

The next day, as Will suspected he might, Rickie made a hurried and inelegant retreat. However, by this time it made little difference to Will what Rickie knew or said. His problem was now solved.

First thing in the morning Will had seen the envelope in the weeds and had plucked it out and had deemed himself satisfied. Remember I said he was a straight man? Well, here's the proof. He went back to Rickie's flat to tell him he was off the hook, but the bloke had already scarpered.

Something was still not clear to Will about what had happened and on this uncertainty he brooded for some days. He suspected this was the wrong money, that wires had somehow got crossed. Neither Asbo nor Scotty reappeared: two other loose ends Will didn't like. After careful reflection, at the end of the week he sold out to a rival for a knock-down price and moved to Amsterdam where he bought a couple of bars. Seems he's doing well there and planning to expand. Smart bloke, people say, runs a tight ship. You know where you are with him.

* * *

Rickie, like Asbo and Scotty, vanished. He was used to moving on but this was the first time he'd run away. The sequence of events appeared simple to him: money had been mis-delivered; someone else, God knows how, had taken it; this man with the dead eyes thought he still had it and would, unless he paid him back, kill him.

The heroin had given him a jolt, too. That was, once again, now his purpose. The RCA could wait. He'd get himself sorted out, de-tox, re-start, re-boot, re-apply.

Sadly, this never happened as Rickie died of an overdose in Leeds six months later.

Not having had an answer to his calls, Pete went round and found the place deserted. He tracked down Rickie's landlord who told him the lease had been up at the end of the month, that Rickie had returned the keys and had taken his few personal possessions. His deposit had covered any dilapidations. If Pete wanted to rent it, he was too late: it had already been taken.

A week later, on the first day of term, Pete called the RCA and discovered Rickie had not taken up his course. They were cross about this. Rickie had, Pete was told, recently been awarded a grant from an arts foundation he had applied to several months before. What were they going to do with the nine thousand pounds that they'd just received?

Pete hung up. The plan had gone to hell. Rickie had grabbed the cash and decided to run off. It was unlike him but there was no other explanation. He felt so let down. The irony was that Rickie hadn't needed Pete's money anyway. Pete asked himself what the hell he'd been thinking of, playing god like that.

Carol was equally depressed. This proved to be the hinge on which their relationship swung. Neither had as much confidence thereafter in each other's judgement. Pete's easy-going positivity became tinged with a dark cynicism; her emotional warmth cooled into something approaching indifference. Before long they were unable to recognise the person they'd fallen in love with. I'm not betraying any confidences when I tell you that within two years they'd got divorced.

Do you want a happy ending? I'm sorry, there isn't one. Unless you liked Will, of course. Will was alright. At the end of such a story, one person generally is happy in accordance with their desires and expectations, if not always with their just desserts.

You've Been so Kind

WILLIAM HARDY ALWAYS took his holidays in August.

Normally he had a fortnight with his sister Ruth, her husband David and their three unpleasant sons. A cheap seaside hotel was usually all they could run to, Ruth being a nurse and David an alcoholic. William came on the understanding that he looked after the kids while their parents went to the pub, Ruth believing that this way David's gargantuan appetite for lager and whisky could be constrained within some apology for family life. The presence of a pharmacist and a nurse was useful as the boys had inherited from their father a facility for getting into fights with people larger than themselves. It seemed an unpromising recipe for relaxation but William enjoyed buying ice creams, taking the children out when Ruth and David were about to row, sweeping up broken glass: in short, fussing about with the consequences of a dysfunctional relationship for which he was not responsible and from which for the rest of the year he was mercifully physically removed.

"Going anywhere nice for your holidays?" Geraldine at his chemist's shop asked.

"Probably go away with my sister Ruth's family. Sam's nearly twelve now, you know."

"Coo."

But this year, the day before they were due to leave, one of the children had fallen ill. Eventually he decided to go on his own. He phoned the hotel in Bognor Regis to explain that rather than being six, they would now be one.

"It's most inconvenient," the woman had sniffed.

"I apologise for the lateness," William said, getting increasingly abject. "I've only just been informed. One of the children has been taken ill."

"Well, it's most inconvenient."

The Hotel Shakespeare was just off the Promenade and narrowly missed having a view either of the sea or of the South Downs. The owners were Mr and Mrs Bernard: she a willowy, dispirited woman who seemed always to have her mind on some sad event in the past; he a silent, balding man with large hands whose hobby appeared to be hammering at pipes in the basement. Just as Mrs Bernard found solace in semi-detached melancholia, so her husband had thrown himself into DIY. Nothing in the hotel worked properly, though whether because of or despite Mr Bernard's interventions was hard to tell. His commitment certainly couldn't be faulted and he was rarely to be seen without his canvas tool bag – stripping wires, lifting floor-boards or marking crosses on the wall with a square, blunt pencil.

Such a scene had greeted William on his arrival. In the act of giving him his key, Mrs Bernard's concentration had transferred itself to the top of a ladder on which her husband was balancing as he tried to disembowel a ceiling rose.

"John, I don't think that...Oh well, I suppose, but..." she had said.

"Of *course* it...Grumph," her husband had replied.

The hotel was really run by Sophie, a formidable woman of about twenty. William fell foul of her on the first morning to do with the system for the front-door key.

"So, if I'm *not* the last person in..."

"Look, it's *very* simple..."

William had no wish to be the last person in. Even if Sophie's system were not daunting enough, early to bed and early to rise had always been his attitude. Bognor Regis was hardly awash with *son et lumiere* displays and he was no astronomer, so what was there to keep him up? Being on his own was proving pleasant. He could re-charge his batteries after twelve months of ministering to

Godalming's warts and boils: a welcome break from routine but without the attendant danger of the unexpected.

This changed on the afternoon of the third day.

She was glamorous, if you liked that sort of thing. The Hotel Shakespeare, for so long adrift on its sluggish tides, was disturbed by the unsettling ripples of her personality. When William first saw her she was talking to Sophie and giving as good as she got.

"I booked, I assure you. Helston, Miriam Helston."

"I've no record," Sophie asserted.

"You don't seem full. I can easily go elsewhere. Quite easily."

"Well, it should have been logged," Sophie said, revealing her objection to be a technical one which Miriam Helston could not possibly have understood.

"Do you have a room or not?"

"Number thirteen," Sophie said sulkily, implying that a guest who had bettered her in an argument about procedures should at least expect some bad luck.

William didn't see her again until dinner, which she ate with a permanently arched eyebrow as if she had never tasted anything quite like it before. Then she went out, returning late and waking up Sophie to let her in. For breakfast she had half a cup of coffee. Then she was gone. Most of the guests were relieved.

An hour later, Una arrived.

William judged her to be in her early forties. She was well-turned out but with the haggard look of impending disaster that people often wore on entering Hopcroft's Chemist's, fresh from the doctor's surgery or a contorted inspection of a troublesome area of their body in the mirror. William, not usually a perceptive man, sensed a 'driven' quality to her.

She was first into lunch and looked up to scrutinise every new arrival, after which her face would cloud with disappointment and, finally, frustration. Half an hour later he surprised her in the act of reaching behind the reception desk.

"Oh." She smiled nervously. "I was looking for..."

"It's Sophie's afternoon off. Mrs Bernard has a nap at about this time. I don't know where Mr Bernard is." He looked round, then lowered his voice. "Hammering away, I suppose." Una gave the smallest smile, her eyes drifting round the drab hallway. William decided to go the whole way and allow himself the liberty of a joke. "He must think there's buried treasure here."

"Buried treasure?"

"Yes. All his digging..." His voice trailed off. If Una had not met Mr Bernard the remark would make no sense, still less be funny. He coughed instead. "Can I help?" he went on, feeling in some way *in loco parentis* of the Hotel Shakespeare.

"Oh no...it was nothing." She paused for a moment, examining William with an expression in equal parts cunning, diffident and miserable. "Actually, yes. I need a chemist's."

William laughed. "30 Godalming High Street."

"I'm sorry?"

"That's my shop."

"I see." She smiled back, in the way people do when they have not recently had much practice at smiling. "I was hoping for somewhere a bit closer."

"There's one just down the road. I notice chemist's shops. It's interesting to see the offers and displays. Get some ideas."

"Oh."

"I'll show you the way. I was going out anyway."

They walked for a while in silence. William did his best to fall in alongside her but she moved with short, erratic steps which made this impossible.

"I don't suppose the hotel's full," Una said.

"I don't think so, no. It's the season of course, but what with the recession..."

Una refused to be side-tracked into talk of the recession. "People probably come down just for the week-end...maybe a night."

"Possibly," William said, unsure if this fledgling acquaintanceship, which he wasn't yet sure he welcomed, depended on his agreeing or disagreeing with the remark.

Una's face reassumed the look of frustration she had worn at lunch. "I was expecting a friend to be here. Well," she laughed loudly, "she's not really a *friend*...I know her vaguely. I heard she was coming down. From someone else."

William nodded. "And you were..."

"Oh, I was coming down here *anyway*" she said quickly.

"I see." William said, not seeing at all. "Well, here's the chemist's. 'Farroley and Sons'. I know George Farroley. We met at a conference."

Una turned to face him. "Did you notice if she did?"

William, who had been considering whether, on the strength of a brief chat three years ago, he might drop in to see Mr Farroley and exchange small talk about contraceptive sales, was confused.

"Who?"

Una almost stamped her foot. "Did a woman check in yesterday?"

"Oh. Yes. Miriam...Helston. I think."

"That's her!"

"She left this morning."

"Left? Did she say where she was going?"

"We didn't speak."

"Might she come back?"

"I shouldn't think so."

"Why not?"

"You should really ask Sophie, or the Bernards."

"Yes, you're right. Anyway: thank you. You've been most kind."

William had abandoned the idea of visiting Mr Farroley. "Are you staying long?" he asked politely.

"That depends," she said.

"Perhaps we'll meet again."

Between six and eight o'clock Mrs Bernard served warm light ale and musty sherry in the front sitting room, thus enabling the hotel to claim the rating of 'Hotel with Bar and Restaurant' in the local guidebooks. At ten to eight William was just raising a glass to his lips when Una came in. She looked flushed and unsteady.

"Hello again," William said.

"I was looking for the bar."

"This is the bar."

"My God."

Mrs Bernard had come in and overheard the last exchange but seemed not at all put out. "We have...beer...and, yes, or...some nice sherry, if you would rather," she said, struggling, against her nature, to create the impression of a situation better than it actually was.

"I...no, nothing for me," Una said. Mrs Bernard shuffled away.

"Did you find your friend?"

Una's face clouded. "No."

"Did you ask Mrs Bernard?"

"No."

William smiled good-naturedly at this paradox.

"But I know where she's staying. It's a bit difficult – look," she went on in a rush, "why not come out? On me?"

"Well, I..."

"Really, my treat. There must be a pub nearby."

It was clear she had steeled herself to be assertive. William had seen it countless times before, often from acned teenagers who had decided that today, come hell or high water, was going to be Clearasil Day. Looked at in this light it seemed churlish to refuse.

They chose the *Drover's Arms* off the Promenade. At nine-thirty William came from the bar with another round. They had been talking around the subject of the mysterious Miriam Helston but Una had not taken the plunge.

"It's so embarrassing," Una said.

"Embarrassing?" William said, employing his best 'do the piles bleed or merely itch?' manner. "Embarrassing in what way?"

"I don't really know her." She sniffed. "I lied to you."

"You did say you didn't know her *very well*," William hastened to reassure her.

"I don't know her at *all*. I've never even spoken to her." She put down her glass. "Look at me. Can you believe it? I'm thirty-nine, married – well, divorced – a professional person, and look at me, behaving like a schoolgirl, and to a complete stranger."

William tried to arrange these confessions into a pattern. The only clue was the divorce. Had Miriam Helston run off with Una's husband?

"Maybe she'll come back," he said.

"That'll make it worse. I'll have to speak to her, explain what I'm doing and... God. I thought I was so in control of everything...then I find myself coming down here. I'm like jelly. I'm not even sure I want to see her at all now."

There was a longish pause.

"I mean, how direct can I be? 'I hardly know who you are but I think I could be in love with you'? There, I've said it."

William's mind reeled. Miriam Helston had been a ploy to engage him in conversation. Then they were off to the pub – and now this. Such a thing had never happened to him. The next move was surely up to him.

"I don't know what to say," he said at last.

She wasn't looking at him. "That's the problem. God, what a mess." They fell silent, locked in their private confusions.

"How about another?" William said at last.

She smiled sadly. "No, I've had enough." They stood up. "But thank you. And you've been so kind. I thought from the first you had a kind face."

William blushed to the roots of his thinning, sandy hair.

As they walked back, William ran over his options. The problem was that he had no experience to draw on. 'Be yourself', he told himself: but then again, when put to the test, was this likely to be good enough? Sadly, he doubted it.

"Thank you for being so kind," Una said when they were back in the hotel. "I've made you miss dinner, I'm afraid. I don't feel like eating. Too much on my mind."

William grinned rakishly. "Same here."

"Well then..." She shuffled at the foot of the stairs, as unwilling to end the conversation as she had earlier been to start it. Emboldened by three pints of beer, William reached forward and kissed her on the cheek.

"Goodnight."

She laughed. If William hadn't known better he might have thought he'd surprised her. "Sweet man." At the top landing she turned and waved.

That night William Hardy slept badly, his mind awash with thoughts of lust which had lain undisturbed since adolescence.

At breakfast he scanned each new face, much as Una had done the previous day, lingering over his cooling tea. Either she had been down before him or else wasn't coming down at all. Avoiding him? It was possible. He was inclined to think the worst. He ran over the exchanges of the previous evening. His face went hot at the thought of the kiss. He began to whistle. Sophie, clearing away plates by the serving hatch, swung round and fixed him with a fierce gaze. William tried to turn the whistle into a cough, not a particularly easy thing to do.

"Did you want anything, Mr Hardy?" Sophie asked.

"No...no," William said.

"Only we're clearing up. I've the places to set for lunch."

William was struck with the appalling vision of a life dominated by other people's meals, an eternity of preparation of indifferent food from which no one derived any benefit beyond the avoidance of starvation.

He hovered in the hall. It was raining. He had nothing to read, nowhere to go. He had nothing to do, except to wait for Una.

On the reception desk was a rack of brochures which displayed Bognor's attractions. He flicked through them like a man being duped by a magician into picking a particular card. The marine park? The leisure centre? The children's zoo? Perhaps the Southdown Olde Crafts Village, the Bognor Regis Regency Experience or Bole's Donkey Sanctuary, each of whose promotions appealed respectively to nostalgia, ignorance and guilt. Like a collection of ill-matched strangers at a cocktail party the leaflets only offered inconsequential insights, each immediately forgettable. Still William flicked through the rack, his mind on other things.

"Ah...oh," Mrs Bernard said in the same breath.

William looked up. She had appeared from somewhere and was standing vacantly behind the desk. William withdrew his hand from the brochures as if from pornography.

"Ooh," Mrs Bernard said, nodding, seeming to understand – there was nothing to see, nothing to do, no need to waste breath with consonants to make the situation more clear.

She made an effort to brighten up. "There are some nice places... were you looking for something...?" Her voice trailed off at the hopelessness of it all. She plucked a brochure out at random. "That's a nice place," she said wistfully.

William examined the flyer. He had never visited a traction engine park and didn't suppose he would do so today. He put it back.

"Oh," Mrs Bernard said, the sadness returning to her pale voice.

"I'm sure it's nice," William said quickly, for he was a kind man. "But I don't think it's quite..." He groped for a suitable phrase.

"Ah," Mrs Bernard said. They were back where they had started.

With a supreme effort she selected another brochure. "Now *that's* nice," she said. "It's nice," she added by way of further explanation.

William examined it. Walcott House was the only surviving 17th century house in Bognor. The foundations dated back to the reign of Edward IV. The property had changed hands numerous times between Bosworth and the Civil War, had been largely destroyed during the Protectorate and rebuilt by Sir William Fitzsymons soon after the Restoration. Extensively enlarged by William's grandson under Queen Anne, the grounds had been laid out in the 1730s by Hubert Campion, student of Bridgman and Under-Master Gardener to George II. These remained substantially unaltered, save for the 19th-century addition of the Rectory Orchard and the plantation of an *enfilade* of yews near the south wall. Of particular interest was the Chapel of Rest in honour of Sir Stephen Fitzsymons, killed at Blenheim. The chancel owed much to the style of nearby Garston Abbey, while the...

"The lady went there," Mrs Bernard said vaguely. "The lady you...you met..."

William put the brochure on the desk. "Where is it?" he asked.

"Where...oh, where ...?" Mrs Bernard replied. She looked at him blankly, then raised both her arms in a hopeless, imploring gesture. She resembled a tragic figure in some Victorian moral lithograph condemning, say, the horrors of drink.

"Don't worry," William said, "there's a map." Mrs Bernard looked so miserable that he added brightly: "I'm good with maps."

"Will you be...back for lunch?" Mrs Bernard asked, wringing her hands. Now she looked more like a sad saint.

"No," William said, feeling determined. It was his holiday, after all. If he didn't want to come back for lunch, he wouldn't. He turned masterfully on his heel and found himself staring at Sophie.

Sophie sniffed. "I'll put it in the book," she said, swishing over to the desk. Mrs Bernard stood back in terror as Sophie made intricate marks in the ledger. She shut the book with a flourish and gave him a tight smile. "No lunch, then" she said.

William was finding it hard to maintain his composure. "Fine," he said as he retreated down the hall. "Thank you."

"Oh, it's no trouble," Sophie said with fierce satisfaction.

William opened the front door and felt the bracing, salty breeze on his face.

Walcott House was a mile out of town with views of both the sea and the South Downs. Despite the season and the overcast skies it was almost deserted. He wandered alone like a shade from room to room, from conservatory to ornamental maze, seeking solace in these lifeless echoes of times past. His mind was a confused blur of Puritanism and priest's holes, Capability Brown and Cromwell, Regency Rakes and Merrie England. He tried to raise his imagination to picture Sir Henry's Hall in times of celebration or reunion; but the minstrels, the foaming flagons of ale and roast suckling pigs, the hearty laughter and tales of derring-do, the candlelit glimpses of ankle and knee all flitted and faded like so many confused and half-remembered scenes from bad period films. The little crimson ropes and 'Way Out' signs were of more comfort: reminders, amongst this misplaced nostalgia, of the ordered times in which he lived. It was Una, Una to whom his thoughts returned. Would she be here or not? Which would be worse: to see her again, or not to? Regret and opportunity both appeared equally appalling.

After a cursory examination of Campion's topiary he made his way indoors, following the signs for 'Refreshments'. He ordered a cup of tea and a sad pastry and sat down by the window. The sun was breaking through the clouds, raking grey-gold rays across the sky. William sipped and nibbled, feeling ever more depressed. Then he looked up. Standing by the counter, a glass of orange juice in her hand, was Una.

"Well," she said, coming over. She gestured at the empty place.

"May I?"

William half stood up, hovered awkwardly in mid-air, sat down heavily. The plastic chair creaked. "Please."

She smiled faintly.

"A nice house, isn't it?" he said as she sat down.

Una looked about her as if she had only just then noticed she was in a house at all. "Yes, I suppose so. I've thinking things over." She sipped her tea. "That was a...nice evening last night. Thank you for being so kind. I'm afraid I talked too much about myself."

"Not at all," William said gallantly. He was about to add something about wanting to hear more, but he hesitated too long and the words refused to arrange themselves in the correct order.

"I felt unhappy," Una said.

William frowned slightly, confused by the tense.

"But now everything's sorted out. I've brushed the whole thing out of my hair."

"Ah," William said. There was something terribly wrong with the situation. None of the imaginary conversations he had played out had anticipated anything like this.

"Yes, it's all straightforward now," Una went on. She looked up, her eyes gleaming with an unnatural vitality. William had seen this kind of look in his shop, often from people coming in with repeat prescriptions for tranquilizers.

"Good," William said after a moment.

They finished their tea. In the most formal possible tones he could muster. William offered to walk her back to the hotel.

"Yes, thank you." She looked at him, and smiled. "You're so kind." Again, William blushed.

The walk was an agony. The problem of physical proximity was impossible to resolve, given his diffidence and her erratic quick-slow walk. Whenever they touched she neither shrunk away nor drew towards him. Her bright, brittle mood was fading. William felt similarly downcast, ever more sure that the whole business had been an alcohol-induced aberration. In this way they walked the mile or so into town, largely in silence.

As they turned off the sea-front Una stopped and pointed.

"Look, the pub last night, remember?"

William remembered very well. It seemed to belong to a remote age in his life when he had, briefly, been exalted. Now it seemed like the physical manifestation of a taunt.

"I could do with a drink," Una said.

"Lovely idea," William said. He thought of the holidays with Ruth and David, forever nipping in and out of pubs at the strangest times of the day. How he wished they had come with him this time, for then all this wouldn't be happening. He wasn't at all sure what exactly *was* happening but he sensed an awful conclusion.

Una downed a gin and tonic very quickly then moved on to brandy. William toyed with an orange juice but, at the third round, ordered a half of bitter.

"Quite the regulars, we're becoming," he said as he sat down.

"I won't be coming back," Una said. "I'm leaving this afternoon."

This was both better and worse than William had feared. He said nothing.

"It got out of control," she said after a pause.

"It could be made easier," he said, wondering how.

Una shook her head sadly. "You've been so kind."

"I wish I could persuade you to stay," William said, pulling at a large whisky ten minutes later.

Una reached out and touched his hand. "Oh, so do I. So do I." She threw herself back into the seat and started to cry softly. "I've been such a terrible, terrible fool."

Tearful women have a body language all of their own and the dialect was quite beyond William's powers to interpret. He caught the barman's eye; then, filled with pale locker-room courage, leaned forward and took her hand. Much to his surprise and somewhat to his alarm she threw herself into his arms, sobbing wildly. He inhaled her perfume and the salty tang of damp skin. They stayed like this for a long moment, until she pulled herself away from him, making an effort to dry her eyes.

"We must go back," she said.

"Why?" William said. "I want to help you. I want..."

"I know."

"I want to...get to know you," he finished lamely. The commonplace was bursting with all the sincerity of his confused heart.

"I know. But you can't. And that makes it worse." She began to cry again.

"Why?" William almost shouted.

"They'll be waiting," she said sadly, blowing her nose.

"Who?" William asked; but Una only shook her head.

They walked back to the hotel in silence. As they reached the last corner, Una turned to him. "You'd better not come in."

William was more sure than ever she was losing her mind. "Why not?"

"Because I don't want you to. Please. Walk round the block, that way." She pointed back the way they had just come. "Please."

William, unused to such emotionally charged assertion, shrugged. He could think of nothing to say beyond the obvious fact that the request was absurd. He knew of men put through hoops by capricious women, of humiliating games played out to no obvious purpose: but he had also heard tell of the strange paths of affection.

"Please," she implored. Then she reached forward and kissed him on the mouth, fiercely, gripping the back of his head with her hand. She pulled away from him, her face streaming, her hair awry, her eyes wild with confusion. "You've been *so* kind," she whispered. She turned and stumbled up the street towards the hotel.

More for the form of the thing William did as she had asked, arriving at the hotel from the opposite direction three minutes later. He turned the corner just as the police car was pulling away.

The foyer was in uproar.

"Really...I can't say...well, they asked...I don't...oh..." Mrs Bernard reassured the guests.

"I said you were with her last night," Sophie said maliciously as William stood dazed on the threshold. "I had to," she added primly.

"Did it happen here?" a beaky old lady asked with tremulous excitement.

"No, of course not," said a horse-faced old woman. "It was at the Majestic on the Front, where she was staying." She cast her eyes round the dingy foyer. "I don't doubt they were overbooked." She looked at Mrs Bernard. "A stop-gap," she added unkindly.

"Yes...oh yes," Mrs Bernard said.

"What's going on?" William asked and everyone tried to tell him at once.

It wasn't until later, after he'd been questioned by the police, that he got the story straight. Miriam Helston had been murdered in her room at the Majestic sometime the previous night. From various evidence...the long and short of it was that Una had confessed to the crime.

"Did she say anything about being...being in...in love with this Miriam Helston?" the policeman asked awkwardly.

William saw now that she had. "Yes."

"Seemed an ordinary woman, your friend," the policeman opined. "Does she have any family, do you know?"

"She mentioned something about being divorced."

"Did she now? Just turned into a lesbian, I suppose," he added philosophically. "Crime of passion." He shook his head. "Strange. Anyway – thank you, sir. We'll be in touch if we need you for the inquest or the trial."

William cut short his holiday and returned to Godalming. By

the second day he couldn't face alone at home so he went into work.

"Coo," Geraldine said. "Back early. Nice time?"

"So-so." He looked round the shop at the familiar displays: Preparation H, Oraldene, Rennies…He allowed himself a slight smile. A customer came in, bought toothpaste, paid, left. The door trilled, swung, caught on the mat in the normal way, slammed. The noises were so familiar he thought his heart would burst.

"You were on your own, yeah?" Geraldine asked.

"Er…yes. I was on my own."

"Wouldn't fancy that," Geraldine said judiciously.

Another customer arrived, then another. Money changed hands, packages were wrapped. William smiled again. He liked to be kept busy, in his shop.

"Coo," Geraldine said just before lunch, "busy today."

"Yes," said William.

"Bet you'd rather be by the seaside." She looked at him more closely. When he had arrived back he looked as if he could do with another holiday. Now, she wasn't so sure.

"Not really," William said with a smile. "It's good to be back."

"Phoo," Geraldine said, casting up her eyes and shaking herself like a young horse. "Thought I might go to Bognor with my nan for the day Saturday. Nice, is it? Bognor?"

"It's alright. But next year we might go somewhere different. It's good to have a change."

"Boring, was it?" Geraldine asked.

William opened his mouth to reply but just then the bell rang and another customer came into the shop.

"Yes, sir," William said. "Can I help you?"

The Collector

IT MUST HAVE been close to midnight when I came back. There were no lights on downstairs so Judy had gone to bed. She doesn't normally stay up when I'm out seeing a seller anyway.

I shifted the sack to my other hand. As I crossed the road I checked both ways. Habit, really. Nothing to worry about. No one around at this time of night, just a couple of drunks arguing further down the street. One of them was complaining, the other one trying to calm his mate down. If it was his mate. Like I cared.

I opened the front door, went in and bolted it. The hall was dark and I felt along the wall for the switch, not the main one but the one that does the light at the top of the stairs down to the basement.

I put the sack down and flexed my fingers. It wasn't heavy but awkward. I should have brought a bag, proper job with handles, but I was only planning on buying two. Couldn't resist them, though, so there were six in here. The sack was all he had. Obviously didn't expect to make that kind of a sale, so had nothing to offer me to transport them. Small point but it made me mark him down as an amateur. Perhaps I shouldn't have paid so much. Amateurs can go two ways – they can be bullied or they hold out for a silly price. With pros, you know where you are. There's leeway and you both haggle but you know and he knows that there's a max and a min. Amateurs have no idea. Still, I've got them now. That's what counts.

I picked up the sack again and opened the basement door. There was another light switch here, one I didn't need to feel for. Left-arm job, up and back to the wall above the door frame. Not where you'd expect. That's the point. Never know when an extra few seconds might make a difference.

The steps went straight down. The basement's deep so there are twenty-four steps. The walls and steps are all rough, dark concrete and the handrails, one on each side, are rusty. It's all sound – I've checked it out, so no need to waste time and money tarting it up.

Once at the bottom there were two more switches, one to kill the stair light and one for the main one in the room. I flicked them both. Here we go, home at last.

I put the sack on the long table in the middle of the basement. As per normal, I spent a few moments looking around me. I knew them all, of course, every one, and it's not likely anyone's going to come down and touch them. Judy knows better than to try. Not many other people come round and for them the door is always locked. Buyers never come here, I go to them. Who does that leave? Just me. This is my place.

I opened the sack and lifted each one out, arranged them on the table and then folded the sack up and put it on the low shelf next to the bags. The collection is neat and organised and I've found it pays to keep everything else squared off as well. It's a good habit, useful to know where everything is. Never know when you might need to lay your hand on something at short notice. Helps not to have to think. Sometimes instinct is all that matters.

Three of them were a bit larger than I remember but that wasn't important. They aren't classified by size. Not by colour, either. Nor age. I can see you're interested.

There's a connection between everything. Most people don't get it, but it's there. It might be no more than a shade of grey here or a curve there. It might be something I feel when I see it for the first time, when I know exactly where it needs to go, next to what, below what, opposite what.

Depending where I stand, I get a different view. I move three feet back and there's a whole different collection there. Some that I saw before I now can't see at all. Others I can see but from the other side. They all have to fit together to make sense. Each view has to make sense. Otherwise, what's the point.

Sometimes I have to move the ones already there to allow for new arrivals. I might see something in Ponders End or wherever and know exactly where it's going to go, if I move this one there and that one over there. Each move, of course, changes every other view. They've all got to work. There's no point in collecting unless you have a bigger picture. So, if I see something that's going to make the picture better, I know I've got to have it. Nothing else matters. I've got to have it. Then I'll bring it back and put it in the right place, like it was always meant to be there. Now it's perfect. It's come home and the world can't hurt it any more. When I'm down here the world can't hurt me either. So I'm home too.

Faintly from upstairs I heard the flush of a toilet, the shutting of a door, light footsteps, then silence. That would be Judy.

I should explain about Judy. She's my wife and I'm her husband so we expect certain things from each other. Unspoken, often as not. No point saying more than you need, something that might give yourself away or commit you. I don't like breaking a promise. Goes against the grain. So, I try to avoid making them.

Anyway, we understand each other. Up to a point. She keeps the house. I bring in the money. Nothing sexist about that, before you start, just the way things are. Something we're both happy with. We don't ask each other questions about how these things get done.

Same with the bedroom stuff. Now and then we do it. Course we do. It's only natural. Thing is, she needs it more than me. She doesn't need to tell me and I don't need to ask. There's no point in throwing a hissy fit about this like you see some blokes do, making a right old scene. After all, if I don't want something why should I go mental about not having it? I want a quiet life and part of that means keeping Judy happy.

So, there are sometimes men about the place. Judy and I have separate rooms we use most nights. When I'm in I'm normally downstairs so it's not an issue. I don't want to spook these guys out, make them think they've walked into some weird free-love set-up. Most men are happy with the idea they're pulling the wool. I don't care. I know what's going on. Anyway, I got bigger fish to fry.

As for Judy, she's sensible. She's got a good situation and doesn't take the piss. You got to respect that.

Last week there was a bit of trouble, though, and this is really where the story starts.

I came back earlier than expected with a heavy bag. She had this young bloke over, Jake I think he was called, not that it matters. When I came in he was down in the hall. He might have been a bit pissed. Thing is, he had his hand on the door going to the basement.

I dropped the bag and charged. Pure instinct. Before he could move I had him round the neck on the floor, his arm pinned behind his back. Nothing too heavy, just minimum force. All that mattered was stopping him going downstairs.

I wasn't sure what to do next. I had the initiative so it was up to me to make the next move. Then he started screaming. Fair enough. Look at it from his point of view – strange house, just got laid, had a few beers, got lost looking for the loo and the next thing he knows he's in an arm-lock.

Then Judy appears, all wide-eyed. We calmed it down. She went back upstairs, I picked up my bag went down to the basement. Don't know where Jake went. Legged it if he had any sense.

We never mentioned the business again. We both knew where we stood.

That night I took extra care looking things over and putting the new stuff out. But there was something missing, something wrong. It wasn't that I thought Jake had gone downstairs. It was the thought that he might have done. That would have spoiled everything. Not because what he might have seen but because this was my place. This was my world. There was a line and he'd crossed it. Fact he didn't know at the time made no difference. He knew now.

I was down there the whole night and I just couldn't shake it. It had all gone wrong. Privacy invaded, a seal broken. Don't think I'm going to go upstairs and beat Judy til she tells me where Jake lives and then go and torture him to death for having infringed. Who and when and why don't matter, or they don't matter to me. It had happened. Or it could have happened. Came to the same thing. Wake-up call.

The next bit you're going to find hard to believe. I've built up this collection for the best part of five years, going to all kinds of dodgy places and spending money and time getting it right. A lot of people in that boat would never part with it, no matter what. Me, I saw things different. It was the moment to let go. There'd be something else, when the time was right. Anyway, it was all in my head. I didn't need photographs, which might take some explaining anyway. Every item, every view, every trick of the light, I could shut my eyes now and see them all just as I wanted them to be. Why did I need the real things? They'd done their job.

So I called Pete. I've bought things from him and he'd put me on to several blokes who got me stuff he couldn't. Pete might have had more idea than most what I had down there but he couldn't have known the whole story. No one could.

Plus, he's the only person who'd see the whole thing for what it was. I trusted him. Trust is important. He'd take the broad view. He could keep it, sell it as it was or flog it big by bit. His choise. Good luck to him.

I fixed a night Judy was out. Pete rocked up on time, a good sign. He was very polite, very respectful. We drank a beer in the kitchen and chatted but I could tell he was beside himself with curiosity. What was he dealing with here? What was he being asked to take on? These things don't come up every day. Once in a lifetime maybe. If then.

"So..." he said.

"Let's go down," I said. "That's why we're here."

We went into the hall. I unlocked the door and did the left-hand routine with the switch at the top of the stairs. Down we went. Most of the basement was in darkness. I led him into the centre of the room and stood him there. He seemed frozen. His eyes must have been slowly adjusting, starting to take it all in. I walked back to the foot of the stairs, my hand on the switch.

"Ready?" I asked. He didn't answer.

Then I turned on the light.

Don't Tell Your Father

"DON'T TELL MY father," Paul said.

"What do you mean?"

"I mean, don't tell that to my father. It'll wind him up even more"

"He's being stupid."

"Yes."

"Pig-headed."

"I know."

"And what's more..."

"I agree with you," Paul said.

Harriet pursed her lips and swung the car round into Cheyne Walk. "I don't see why he's making such a fuss about it."

"Look – I agree with you," Paul said again. They paused for the traffic, then turned left, by Thomas More's church and into a street barely wide enough for two Volvos to pass. Stained with age and bird droppings, the statue of the great Humanist stared gloomily out across the Embankment and the sludge-sluggish Thames. Paul stared gloomily back.

"We might want to get married *one* day," he added peevishly.

"That's not the point. Of course I might. *We* might. But the more he goes on and on and on about it, the more vile the idea sounds."

Paul winced. It seemed appalling that, thanks to his father's obsession, they were on the threshold of argument about a matter in which they were in fact in agreement.

"I really don't understand why he's so fixated about our getting married," Harriet went on.

"That's the way he is. Morals are everything to him."

"Well, I resent the idea that we're so...so immoral."

"By his standards we are, I suppose."

"Well, he doesn't have to inflict his morals on us."

"I'm sure he doesn't mean to," Paul said.

"Of course he does. That's just what he means to do."

"Well, I suppose he does, really," Paul conceded.

Harriet pulled up outside an elegant eighteenth century town house that was just like all the other elegant eighteenth century town houses in the street.

"Well, here we are," she said, wrenching up the hand brake.

"He can't help it," Paul said. "He is what he is. He means well."

Harriet shrugged, as if to indicate that she thought what he was saying was drivel but that she wasn't prepared to argue the toss at present. Paul was relieved she did not wish to continue the row on the threshold of his parents' house, particularly on such a familiar and insoluble topic.

"Harriet, darling," his mother said as she opened the door. "How are you? Not too tired yet? You've just missed Gramps," she added.

Paul adored his grandfather, and always had done. For as long as he could remember his father and his grandfather had been in opposition in obscure ways which, even now, he understood only imperfectly.

"Don't tell your father," his grandfather would say as he tucked a pound note into Paul's pocket after an outing from school.

"Father, you spoil the boy! It's not good for him," Paul's father would say if he discovered this secret gift.

Paul was never sure why it wasn't good for him, and his father's explanations had only confused him further.

Paul's grandfather was a spry, wry, mischievous character with a colourful past and an eccentric taste in clothes. His principal stock-in-trade was flirtatious irony and little he said could be taken at its face value. This had the effect utterly of confusing a world inclined to treat remarks by someone of his age either as nuggets of intense, if irrelevant, wisdom, or else as the ramblings of a senile fool. In this respect, no one was more confused than Paul's father.

Paul's father, Lawrence, was a serious man and had devoted his life to overcompensating for his own father's flippancy. Time and again, Paul had witnessed his father confounded and infuriated almost beyond endurance by his grandfather's casual indifference to conventions. At Lawrence's wedding, or so Paul had heard, his father had during his speech affected several times to forget his son's name; on another more recent occasion he had joined a mystic sect and been recognised delivering their handbills only two streets away. Only three months before he had bought a large motor-cycle. Paul's grandmother seemed not at all concerned by all this, but to Lawrence the whole thing was an ever-changing torture. The old man would listen to his son's baleful admonishments with great calm, then pretend to fall asleep just before the conclusion. Paul had long delighted in this vigorous and discordant relationship. He suspected that even his mother found it amusing at times, although of course she was far too nice to say so out loud.

As Lawrence was never taken seriously by his father, and as none of the old man's foibles were actually illegal, Lawrence began out of frustration to mount a secret propaganda campaign against him. This would take the form of accusations in themselves minor but calculated through repetition to convince people that his father was deeply peculiar. By a strange reversal of logic he believed this would help dissipate the social opprobrium with which he felt, quite wrongly, his family was tainted due to his father's behaviour. The subject of these tirades would change from time to time, but one theme always reappeared. This was the matter of his father's ties; or 'neckties' as Lawrence called them, an archaic word unfamiliar to his younger relations who were thus even more confused by the meaning which lay behind Lawrence's accusations as well as the extraordinary ferocity with which they were prosecuted.

"Why the devil can't father wear a decent necktie once in a while?" he would growl after a family gathering.

"I really didn't notice it, dear," his wife would murmur.

"I'm surprised. It's a disgrace."

It truth, the old man's ties were among the least peculiar part of his wardrobe. It was possible he might have sported the colours of a regiment, or club, or Cambridge college to which he had never belonged, but no accusation was ever specified by his son. Lawrence merely lay before the world the self-evident fact that there was something badly wrong with his father's neckties and if people couldn't see what it was then it was their own damned fault.

"Suppose I'd better get my father a decent necktie for Christmas."

"Yes, darling."

"Not that there's any point, though – the stupid man would never wear it." But he always did buy his father ties, and his father never did wear them.

"I thought he could at least have worn the necktie I gave him last year instead of that awful thing. Looked like a dishcloth."

Paul suspected that his father would on each occasion buy two identical ties, keeping one pinned in a scrapbook with the date and circumstance of the gift written alongside as a reminder.

"Lovely necktie I bought you two Christmases ago, father. Would go well with that shirt. Can't think why you never wear it."

"But this is my drinking tie."

"Drinking tie? What the hell are you talking about?"

"When you get to my age you dribble down the front of your shirt all the time."

"Rubbish."

And the old man would grin, and wink at any attractive ladies present, and pretend to dribble down the front of his shirt.

"Really, father," Lawrence would hiss, "it's too much."

"We'll have to get him into a home," he said to his wife as they were getting into bed.

"Rubbish. Everyone loved him."

"Did you see the state of his necktie?"

Paul's grandfather clearly had knowledge of the world which had eluded Lawrence. Perhaps this was a natural result of a long and eventful life, perhaps of a specific secret long kept hidden from his son: a bit of both, Paul suspected. Lawrence found it had to accept that at fifty-nine he was still not fully master in his own house. Even though neither his peculiar father nor his capricious son lived with him, both had the capacity for throwing his life into turmoil. Of the two, Paul was the easier to handle: and it was on Paul that Lawrence fixed his liverish gaze after the formalities of tea had been taken. He helped himself to a brandy and soda and sat down.

"So, what are you two doing about getting married?" he asked after a short and, to him, impressive pause.

Harriet had picked up a magazine and was flicking through it in a bored way.

"We thought we might...one day," she said.

"That's hardly good enough."

"Why not? No one else seems very bothered," Paul said.

"I'm not interested in what everyone else thinks!" his father snapped. "I suppose you're thinking of your mother, or," – and here he paused with morbid resignation – "your grandfather."

Paul shrugged.

"Let me tell you that my father is a moral degenerate."

"In what way?"

"In every way. In every way possible. He drinks too much. He smokes too much. He knows the most peculiar people. He used to take drugs. I know that for a fact. Definitely."

"What kind of drugs?"

"I don't know. Pills of some sort."

"Everyone takes pills. You take pills, Dad. What's the problem?"

"There's also that business of the motor-bike. A man of his age... It's such a worry for me, and your mother. And the *clothes* he wears – he looks like a French artist, or a mad old fool."

"He's certainly got some nice ties," Paul said.

There was a pause. Paul's father appeared to consider whether to develop this entrancing idea or leave it alone completely in the interests of advancing his main theme.

"You know what I think about your grandfather's neckties," he said at last. "The point is that even he did the decent thing when he met your grandmother. Even in those days I'm sure they...I know it wasn't the accepted thing to have...to have relations...of that kind... anyway, I was born quite shortly after they met...as you probably know." He paused, distracted by the flow of euphemisms. "The point is that Harriet is now, what, two, three months?"

"Four months."

"Four! There you are! Four months pregnant. You haven't even made plans."

"We've made lots of plans," Harriet said. "We just haven't made any plans to get married."

Lawrence turned on her coldly. "I don't think that's a satisfactory answer."

"Oh..." Harriet said, employing a dreamy tone of voice which Paul knew to be far more menacing than his father could ever guess. "Well, it's good enough for us."

Paul stood up. "Love, why don't you...why don't you see if mum... if my mum wants..." With horror he realised his clumsy phrases were sounding just like his father's.

Harriet threw down the magazine and strode over to the door. "I need to go in about ten minutes, okay?"

Father and son listened to Harriet's footsteps receding down the stairs.

"Are you *sure* you want to marry her?" Paul's father asked.

"What are you talking about?" Paul said, wondering if first to deal with the assumption that they were getting married, or the implication that he might not want to do so.

"Well, she seems very hot-tempered."

"Hot-tempered? She's pissed off! You drag us over here to talk about something we didn't want to discuss, then you insult her! Plus she's pregnant, for God's sake!"

"Starting to get broody, I suppose," his father said. He rounded off the remark with a vile locker-room wink, as uncharacteristic as it was gauche. Paul realised he was making a pathetic attempt to ingratiate himself, man-to-man.

"It's got nothing to do with being broody. Anyway, that happens before you get pregnant. It's got to do with common politeness. Why are you so bothered, anyway?"

His father's face had now assumed what his grandfather called his 'Jesuit expression', in which guilt, stubbornness and a belief in his moral rectitude were mixed in roughly equal proportions. From experience Paul knew that the situation was now unlikely to be resolved without one of them losing their temper.

"I just know it's the right thing to do. Got to give the child a name."

"It's going to have a name. Mine, probably. Ours, for that matter. I like the name Frobisher. Harriet has always said that being called Adams was hell at school because she had to go up and do things first. Like vaulting over the horse in P.E."

His father was in no mood to be distracted by levity. "You know what I mean."

"I'm not sure I do. Who would this wedding be for, anyway – us or you?"

"By 'you' I presume you are including your mother," Lawrence said sententiously.

"Mum doesn't care one way or another!"

"Well, she ought to."

"You have got to face the fact that she doesn't," Paul insisted. "I presume you would regard her as being moral?"

"I don't know why you keep running down morals," his father said peevishly. He had suddenly exploded into life at the prospect of discoursing on his favourite subject. Paul languidly lit a cigarette. "It's one thing to have no morals, to be amoral, but to flaunt them – as you seem to plan to...that's something different altogether. It's no basis for a relationship. You have no commitment, no sense of responsibility sanctioned by all the tenets of society. God knows there are some things wrong with our society – I'd be the first to admit it – but it does set down rules which make you realise where you stand. If family values mean anything at all, then I think you should realise that..."

Paul held up his hand, determined to stop the flow of words before both of them lost their grip on what his father was talking about. "You're saying five or six different things, Dad. Morals, society, commitment, family values, our child...what I do understand is that you feel if the baby is born out of wedlock then he or she will be tainted in some way. Morally."

"Yes."

"Frankly, I don't agree. So where do we go from here?"

His father considered this. "I was hoping to be able to settle some money on the child."

"This is like a Georgette Heyer novel. So you're threatening to cut me off without a penny?"

His father writhed in his seat.

"Actually, I'm not that bothered. You've always wanted me to make my own way, and I have. I've got money of my own. So has Harriet, for that matter."

His father now looked severely uncomfortable. "What I meant was..." He paused, trying to get a grip on his thoughts.

"Well, I think your attempt to bribe me was shockingly immoral."

The door swung open. Paul's grandfather came in, followed by Harriet and his mother: and with that the atmosphere immediately improved. The old man was wearing a double breasted suit, a yellow waistcoat, an MCC tie and a monocle and had waxed his moustache to two fine points. Salvador Dali might have looked something like this if attending an interview for a job with a merchant bank.

"Gramps! I thought you'd gone!"

"Well, here I am, back again. Who's being immoral? Your father, I suppose.." He sat down on the sofa, stretched out his legs and winked at everyone in general.

Lawrence shuddered then, through force of habit, focused his eyes on his father's bright tie.

"How's the test match is going?" Paul's grandfather asked.

"England were eighty-one for eight last I heard," Paul said.

"For *eight*?" The old man fingered his tie and met his son's gaze. "So, what's all this immorality? Let me judge. As the oldest person present, no other reason. I'm no expert, you understand."

Paul smiled. "We were talking about getting married."

"Really?" For a moment his grandfather had lost his composure. There was a brief pause.

Lawrence, the only one with a standard response to any situation involving his father, reacted first. "I didn't know you were a member of the MCC," he said, glaring at the egg-and-bacon tie.

The old man seemed not to have heard him.

"And your father thinks this would be a good idea, I suppose?"

"Of course I do! It's not fair on the children!"

Paul's grandfather gave Lawrence a peculiarly searching look. "No," he said slowly, "I don't believe it is. Paul, do you love Harriet?"

"Yes," Paul replied, reddening less from embarrassment than from the unexpected turn the conversation had taken. "Of course I do."

"Harriet," he went on, moving round in the sofa so as to look at her full in the face, "do you love Paul?"

"I sure guess so," she replied, mock-American.

"Well then," Paul's grandfather said, holding out his arms, "why the hell not? It's an excuse for a party. And what a party we'll have."

The mood had changed so rapidly, so completely, that Paul and Harriet both found themselves laughing. Paul stood up and went over to her, one hand holding hers, the other gently resting on her stomach.

"A double celebration," his grandfather went on.

"Double?" Paul's father asked sharply.

The old man looked confused, as if he'd been caught out in some way.

"The wedding and the baby, of course," he said quickly.

"Do you know," Paul said, "we might just do that."

* * *

Everyone disagreed as to how the mix-up had occurred. Harriet blamed Paul's father, who blamed the invitation printers, who blamed Paul, who blamed the registrar, who blamed Harriet's mother, who blamed Harriet...the long and short of it was that, at twenty past noon on the appointed Saturday, Paul, his best man, Harriet and Harriet's great-aunt were drinking pints in the Rose and Crown up the road from the registry office, believing the ceremony to have been fixed for half past, whereas in fact...

"Can't think where they've got to," Paul's father said, checking his watch. "they're over twenty minutes late."

"The traffic," Paul's mother said vaguely.

"They've probably had cold feet. Or she's gone into labour. Ha!" He laughed bitterly at the thought of this fresh moral humiliation.

"Darling, she's got five months to go."

"I know that, for God's sake. And where the hell are my parents?

They were here a moment ago."

"I don't know, dear. Maybe they've gone to look for them."

"He's a hopeless man. Quite hopeless. We really must see about getting him into a home."

"I really don't think..."

"And did you see his necktie? *Most* unsuitable for a wedding."

* * *

In the pub, Paul was ordering a round of double scotches. "It's only just twenty-five past," he said. "I think it's important to turn up dramatically late. Five minutes should do it. Keep them waiting five minutes. Cheers!"

"Cheers."

"Cheers, darling."

"Where's my speech? Oh hell, I've lost my speech!"

* * *

"Where the hell are they?" Lawrence was standing with his wife on the registry office steps. He glanced over his shoulder at the fifty or so people crowded inside: in front of him an even larger group was assembled for another wedding, superficially interchangeable with those within but all utter strangers to him. He felt lost, unable to cope. What did one do in these situations? His moral code gave him no guidance.

"Mr Frobisher?"

"Yes? What's happened? What?"

The man smiled blandly, wringing his hands like an undertaker. "I'm the registrar. Mr Rose. It's just to say that we do have another wedding...perhaps if you and your party could wait in the ante-room...it's more than possible we could conduct your ceremony after that, as I have had a cancellation..."

"A cancellation? It sounds like a bloody hotel!"

"Lawrence, *please*."

"A sudden illness, I believe," Mr Rose placidly continued. "Or perhaps 'postponement' would be a better word. As indeed in your case...a postponement. I'm sure a misunderstanding, or the traffic..."

"The traffic, yes. I said it would be the traffic," Paul's mother said.

"It happens all the time."

"*All* the time?"

"*Some* of the time," Mr Rose corrected himself, still smiling. "A postponement, due to unforeseen...it does happen. It has, indeed, happened. Twice today. Twice in three weddings, in fact. So...it does happen, you see." At this point another man came up to Mr Rose and whispered in his ear. Mr Rose raised his eyebrows a few times, nodded, shrugged, nodded again.

"Excuse me, please. If you could arrange to move your party to, er...just a *postponement*, of course...thank you *so* much..."

So they ushered everyone out of the main hall and into a side room which smelt of floor polish and tom cats, and waited for the bride and groom to arrive.

"Where the *hell's* my father?" Lawrence asked again.

*   *   *

Paul, Harriet, the best man and Harriet's great-aunt stepped out of the pub.

"There's a back way," Paul said. "Comes out by the side entrance. Come on." Paul realised he felt nervous. The whole event was going to be over almost before it had begun, and it had suddenly become important to him not to miss a second of it. The alcohol-bravado had evaporated. He seized Harriet's hand.

"Ow!"

"Come on!"

They turned one corner, then another.

"There it is!" Paul said, relieved. They walked up to the side entrance and peered in. The doorway led into a small room, in which there were three people. His grandfather and grandmother were writing something in a book. The registrar said something. His grandfather and grandmother kissed.

"Gramps!" Paul said, "what the hell are you doing?"

"Ah," his grandfather replied, letting go of his wife's hand and walking towards Paul. "A good question. You were late, by the way."

Paul looked at his watch. "Two minutes."

"Thirty-two minutes, I'm afraid."

"Oh my God."

"Your father seems to think it's my fault, of course."

"Is it?"

"Not at all. But I guessed what had happened. You did mention something about half-twelve the other day, but I didn't really take it in. I imagined you were in the pub."

"We were."

"Good. We intend to do some drinking ourselves."

"Did you tell my father about what you thought had happened?"

"No."

"Why not?"

"We had a better idea."

"What are you talking about? What's going on?"

"It seemed a shame to waste a good registry office. We'd have preferred a church, of course, but you have to take your opportunities where you can find them. *Carpe diem*, you know. And Mr Rose here was so understanding..."

Mr Rose bobbed and ducked in the background.

Paul blinked a couple of times. Maybe the old man had slipped his anchor after all.

"Aren't you going to congratulate us? I'd like you to be the first. It's not often your grandson is present at your wedding."

"At your wedding?" Paul said. "But...but you're married! You got married ages ago." He thought of his father. "You must have done. Obviously."

"We didn't, actually," his grandmother said with a soft smile. "We never got round to it."

"You know how it is," her husband continued. "You meet, have a baby, fight in a war, buy a house...somehow there didn't seem to be time."

"But we always planned to," his wife said.

"Oh yes. If only for Lawrence's sake, poor boy. It would never do for him not to have a name. Look. You don't seem to believe me." He thrust a certificate into Paul's shaking hand. Peter Marius Frobisher, retired, aged seventy-five, had without doubt married Jane Rachel Thomas, spinster, also aged seventy-five, on Saturday 28th June at Chelsea Registry Office, Thomas Rose as Registrar, James Herbert Smith as witness. It was all there in black and white.

Everyone examined the certificate. "Who's James Herbert Smith?" Paul asked idiotically.

"My colleague," Mr Rose said. "He was kind enough to assist."

"Do you know," Paul's grandfather went on, this time more thoughtfully. "I feel bad about the whole business."

Paul slowly raised his eyebrows, wondering if the old man had had second thoughts and was now about to seek an annulment.

"About your father," he went on. "It wasn't fair to behave as I did. God knows how, when he was about thirty he became so serious about the whole business of conventional morality. He didn't get that from me. It seemed to us as if he knew about his illegitimacy and was over-compensating."

Paul blinked a couple of times. This wasn't at all the conversation he was expecting on this, his would-be wedding day.

"I was over-compensating too," his grandfather went on. "At first, I was annoyed. Then I was amused. Then it became a habit. The trouble is, your dad worries about what the world thinks of him.

I don't. It really isn't important, you know. Do remember that. But I don't want to hurt him any more. I see now I have done. When we came in at the end of that argument you were having, that gave us the idea. We *had* to make an honest man of him somehow." He paused and looked away, almost sadly; then brightened again. "This unexpected opportunity was too good to miss. As a newly-married man, I'll be turning over a new leaf. But, look – We can't tell him about this. After all these years, that would be *too* much. It's enough that it's happened, don't you think?"

Paul and Harriet both shook their heads, then nodded, then shrugged: the closest either could come to any lucid reaction.

From down the side-street familiar voices and faces were coming their way, led by an angry-looking, red-faced man in a morning suit perhaps one size too small for him.

"There they are!" Lawrence said. "Paul, what the hell's going on?"

Paul's grandfather leaned forward and pushed the marriage certificate into Paul's pocket as if it were a clandestine pound note. "Don't tell your father," he said with a wink.

The Outing

WE WERE SITTING in the staff room, Tony Jefcut, Madge Smith, Mr Frobisher and me, when Tony suggested we went to the pub.

"For a quick one after work," he explained.

Mr Frobisher looked at Madge, and laughed.

"Why not? The night is young," he said. "Even if I'm not."

So we went. On the way we ran into Mr Chivers from Planning and Tony asked him, even though they hardly know each other, just a 'hello' on the stairs, if that, but he said he'd like to come to the pub as well.

We made quite a party, the five of us. I hadn't been to a pub for years.

We ordered lager, except for Madge who said she wanted white wine, and sat down. Mr Frobisher sat next to Madge, with Tony on the other side of her and me and Mr Chivers opposite on stools.

Mr Frobisher was a large man with bad teeth and a habit of breathing through his nose when telling a story. He drunk his beer with gusto, speckles of foam catching on his upper lip. The rest of us sipped our drinks. I tried to relax.

Tony stretched out his arm behind Madge's head so she couldn't see what he was doing. After a while he produced a nine of clubs from behind her ear.

"Neat trick," Mr Frobisher said. "Where did you learn that?"

"Fellow I know," Tony replied.

Tony was younger than the rest of us and had a reputation for fast living. He owned a car, for one thing, and often came in to the office complaining of a hangover. He also told jokes, rather blue ones. All in all he was a bit of a wag.

"You're a bit of a card, Tony," I said.

Tony looked at me blankly.

"My uncle Bernard used to do card tricks, at the seaside," Mr Frobisher said.

"Really," Tony said.

Mr Frobisher told a story about his uncle Bernard's card tricks which I found hard to follow. "That was a good trick of yours though, out of the ear. Good one."

"Funny, that," Madge said, "Because I had a conjurer who was an uncle...I mean an uncle who was a conjurer."

"Careful, now," Mr Frobisher said.

Madge giggled.

"That's not the same thing, you know," Mr Frobisher said.

Madge laughed.

"No...I don't know why I said that."

Mr Frobisher laughed.

"Too much wine," I joked.

Madge looked at me. "I don't think so," she said.

"Not yet, anyway" Mr Frobisher said.

Madge laughed.

Tony yawned. "So what are we all doing tonight?" he asked.

Madge didn't know. Mr Frobisher looked at Madge and said that he didn't know either. Mr Chivers said there was something on the telly he wanted to see. I didn't say anything.

"We could go to a club," Tony said.

"What sort of club?" Madge said.

"Just an idea," Tony said.

"Not a blue club, I hope," Madge said with a giggle.

"Yes, one of your blue clubs," Mr Frobisher said.

"I don't go to blue clubs," Tony said.

"Course you do," Mr Frobisher said with a wink. "Young man like you."

"It's a new place, just off the High Street. They've got jazz there."

"Didn't know you liked jazz, Tony," said Mr Frobisher.

"Don't mind it."

"Didn't you used to play the trumpet?" Madge asked Mr Chivers.

Mr Chivers stirred in his seat. "Long time ago," he mumbled. "And it was a brass band, anyway. You know, brass band stuff."

"Did you used to play in the park here?" Madge asked.

"No. It was back home. Years ago now."

"Maybe I saw you, in the park," Madge went on. "I used to go up there with a friend at the weekends."

"Courting couple, eh?" said Mr Frobisher.

"Hardly! Not likely! It was Claire Morgan." Madge laughed.

"Going to meet your boyfriends, I suppose," Mr Frobisher said, and nudged her slightly.

"Our fathers didn't like us having boyfriends," Madge said.

"More's the pity, eh?" Mr Frobisher said. "Different now, though?"

"It was twenty years ago, give or take," Madge explained.

"He'd let you out know, I suppose?" Mr Frobisher went on.

"That the Claire Morgan I know?" Tony asked.

"She used to work at the council if that's who you're thinking of," Madge said. "Blonde hair. Quite tall."

"And bit whatjumacallits," Mr Frobisher said. He took another pull at his beer and sat back in his seat grinning, for some reason, at me.

"We were at school together. Then she got a job at the council, working for Mrs Heaver in Planning."

"The famous Mrs Heaver," Mr Frobisher said.

"In Planning?" I asked. Mr Frobisher was still looking at me. I felt I ought to say something.

There was a pause, and we all sipped our drinks.

"That's your pigeon, planning, isn't it?" Mr Frobisher asked Mr Chivers.

"For my sins."

"Doesn't leave you much time for playing the trumpet, I shouldn't think," Madge said.

Mr Frobisher laughed.

Madge took another sip of her drink. "I'm surprised I never saw you at the park, because we used to go there. Claire's father played the oboe and she used to bring him his sandwiches at the weekend. What sort of stuff did you play, when you played the trumpet?"

"Brass band stuff, mostly," said Mr Chivers. He shifted his weight.

I always forget that he's got a problem with his legs which makes it difficult for him to sit comfortably. He's got a terrible temper as well. You wouldn't think so to look at him, but he has.

No one said anything for a bit.

"How about this club, then?" Tony said.

"Thought rock music would be more your line, Tony," Mr Frobisher said.

"Do you like rock music, Tony?" Madge asked.

"Don't mind it," Tony said.

"Jazz, you say?" Madge asked. I could see that she was quite keen to go.

"I don't really have enough breath any more," Mr Chivers said. "You want breath, not spit."

Madge and Mr Frobisher laughed.

"That threw me a bit, that did" Madge said. "I thought we were discussing this club of Tony's, and then there's you talking about spitting!"

"Hardly," said Mr Chivers coldly.

"Sounded like it to me," Mr Frobisher agreed jovially. "'not enough spit' were the words, I think. Or am I wrong?"

"Yes, you were. I was talking about playing the trumpet."

"Still up there in the attic, gathering dust, I'll be bound," Mr Frobisher went on.

I considered kicking Mr Frobisher under the table as Mr Chivers seemed to be about to get into one of his moods.

"I can still blow a few notes," Mr Chivers went on doggedly.

"You need the spit for it, I've heard," Tony said, winking at Madge.

"Oh, Tony," she said, laughing. "Don't."

"So who's coming, then? Tony asked. "It's cheap drinks before nine. Half price shorts, that sort of thing."

"You know a lot about this club, Tony," Madge said. "Owned by a friend of yours, is it, by any chance, mmm?"

"That's right, drumming up business," Mr Frobisher said.

Tony didn't look pleased. "Is, as a matter of fact," he said. He finished off his beer with a gulp. "I'm off, anyway."

"That the fellow who taught you the card trick?" Mr Frobisher asked. "The old ten of hearts out of the ear?"

"Was, actually. He plays the trumpet, thought he'd try and get a jazz club off the ground."

"The trumpet, eh?" Mr Frobisher said, turning to Mr Chivers. "Daresay you could give him a few tips."

"I can still get a tune out of it, I shouldn't wonder," Mr Chivers said stiffly.

"They might call you up on stage," Madge said. "If Tony slips them the word. You could do that, couldn't you, Tony?"

Tony gave a thin smile and quickly checked his watch.

"'And on trumpet – Mr Chivers'," Mr Frobisher declaimed.

"Mr Chivers from Planning," Madge said.

"Mr Chivers from Planning," Mr Frobisher agreed. They both laughed.

Tony stood up, jangling his car keys. "Anyway – I'm off. Who's coming?"

"I might look in," Madge said.

"We could have one more drink first, surely?" Mr Frobisher said. "My round."

"Said I'd be there by seven," Tony said. He turned to Mr Chivers. "It's not all modern stuff."

"Your kind of thing," Madge agreed, nodding at Mr Chivers.

"Anyway, cheap drinks," Tony reminded them.

"Probably not up his street," Mr Frobisher said, tapping Madge on the elbow. "He prefers the old oumpah-oumpah."

Mr Chivers looked at Madge, then at Mr Frobisher, then back to Madge again. His expression was very fierce.

"Do you know, I think I might come. Hear some trumpet again. I can always leave if I don't like it."

Mr Frobisher looked at Madge but she didn't say anything about this one way or the other. He moved slightly away from her. Now it was him that looked annoyed.

"That's the spirit," Tony said. "We can go in the car. There's room for four."

"Your Jag," Mr Frobisher said, rather bitterly.

"Wish it was," Tony said with a grin. Then he looked at me. "Oh – do you want to come?"

"It's not my sort of thing, really," I said.

"OK," Tony said, and looked at the others. "All set?"

Everyone else stood up, although Madge had hardly touched her wine. We left the pub.

"Night-night, Tony," the barman called after us.

"See you tomorrow, then," Mr Frobisher said to me as he squeezed into the back of Tony's Mini. "Back at the treadmill."

"Madhouse, more like," Madge said from the back seat. I watched them drive away. Then I went home.

The following morning, I heard that Mr Chivers had got into an argument at the club with Mr Frobisher and had been asked to leave. Also, Tony had crashed his car on the way home as a result of which he had been given the breath test by the police.

"It's a write-off, apparently," Miss Collins said.

"Really?" I said. Actually, I was quite shaken.

"And did you hear about Mr Frobisher and whatshername, the lady from Amenities?"

"Who?"

"The one who had that dog."

"Oh – Madge Smith. No."

"Well, apparently they came in together this morning, grinning like monkeys, the pair of them."

"Well, well." I went back to my desk and sat down. What a night! And there I'd been, right in the middle of it all. Well, sort of.

Meeting Stanley

"NOW, JOAN, DO help with this case. Where's Beryl?...Beryl, take this bag. There. Oh, Mary, have you the tickets?"

Mary had walked a few steps away from the confusion of the disgorging taxi and was watching the crowds flooding in and out of Waterloo station. She turned to her elder sister. "No, I haven't," she said quietly, wiping a strand of blond hair from her face. "You had them."

"Are you sure?"

"Quite sure."

Linda Salter threw up her hands in a gesture of vast despair and began frenzied and incomplete searches of various bags. Mary sighed and turned back to her view of the station concourse. She slipped into a reverie.

"Now, children, you must help! Millie, stop singing. And your Aunt Mary must help too. Now...ah, here they are. Thank goodness! Beryl, help granny out..."

Granny need no help, from Beryl or anyone else, but graciously permitted her eldest grandchild to offer an arm. She stepped onto the pavement, smoothing her billowing linen skirts.

The unloading was now complete. Linda Salter considered the luggage, and the capacity of her family to move it, with foreboding. In their various ways they were quite useless. Mary was the worst, always a few paces behind or in front of everyone else; or else stood stock-still, as now, staring into the middle distance like an idiot child of thirty. Beryl, who was sixteen, needed to test the graceful motion of her long limbs and hated to be burdened with anything. The three younger children were obviously also quite useless. Her mother, who was in fact almost strong enough to carry most of the luggage and several of the children on her back, was seventy-one and therefore quite useless as well. Mrs Salter sighed. Apart from herself, everyone was quite useless.

"Are we going on a steam train?" eight-year-old Millie asked happily.

Her elder sister Joan rolled her eyes. "They don't have steam trains on this line now, silly. It's diesels."

"Oh," said Millie, shamed as always by Joan's rebukes.

"Class-two diesels," Joan went on. Joan was ten.

"I hate steam trains," five-year-old George said, bravely trying to hold Joan's aloof gaze.

"That's because you're stupid," said Joan.

"No I'm not." George said. His little face was reddening with the effort of arguing with his brain-box of a sister. Joan saw he was about to cry, and so pinched him.

George started to cry.

"Children, oh children," Mrs Salter said ineffectually. "Now, *mother...where's* Granny gone?"

Linda's mother reappeared with a porter and issued instructions as to how the luggage should be arranged on the trolley. Linda flapped about like a large green moth, trying to find fault with some detail. With the porter in the lead and Mary bringing up the rear, the Salter family cut loose from its moorings by the taxi rank and sailed into the storm of humanity before them.

"Now, *when* does the train leave? The train for Corfe Castle. The Purbeck branch. Porter, do you know?"

The porter paused and produced a stained almanac. "Corfe... Castle. Here we are." He mentioned platform numbers, times of connections at Basingstoke and Bournemouth, the availability of refreshments *en route*. Linda despaired. It was all too complicated, and her with *everything* to manage.

"We have half an hour, Linda," her mother said. "We can have some tea."

"Oh, *tea*," said Linda Salter, as though that might be a suitable way of wasting time for those with no responsibilities.

"Would you like a drink, children?" their grandmother asked.

"I'd like orange," Millie said, and started to sing to herself, skipping slightly in time to the rhythm. Joan nodded, her mind on other things. George, who organised his life around the idea of being as unlike any of his sisters as possible, shook his head.

The pretty Beryl said: "I'd like some tea." After all, she was nearly grown up. Mary had vanished. Linda looked round in desperation. If the train was called now, what would they do? They'd just have to go without her.

The porter deposited them outside the refreshment room. "I suppose we *do* have time? If Mary were here she could go and ask..."

"I shall go, Linda."

"But, mother..." Linda felt that sending her mother to enquire of train times was wrong in some way; but she had already set off. "Oh – *do* find out!" Linda called after her.

Linda Salter watched Millie and Joan playing: that is to say, Joan was giving complicated instructions to Millie that she was clearly making up as she went along. George was sitting swinging his legs.

Linda considered George. It would be too much to say he was a problem but he often seemed remote. She did not blame herself. Things had been hard after Stanley had left and the three girls were, of course, so demanding.

Linda wondered how different things would have been if Stanley had still been with them. Well, they were all going off to see him at his new house at the seaside, so at least the children would have that to keep them occupied for the week. As for her and Stanley, they could talk, again: and then – who knows?

"Mummy," Millie wailed, her heart-shaped face stained with

tears of failure, "Joan wants me to play dinosaurs and I don't know how."

Linda could think of no obvious solution to this. "Girls," she said at last, "can I trust you with a half-crown?"

"Yes," Joan said promptly. Millie smiled, wiping away sticky tears.

Linda gave instructions as to the purchase of orange drink and tea and sent them off to the counter. She was alone with George. She smiled at him but couldn't think of anything to say.

Instead, she looked towards the refreshment counter. The place was filling up with men, rough types; soldiers, perhaps. Millie was quite capable of striking up a conversation with a stranger and probably giving him the half-crown if she felt sorry for him. What was to be done?

Mary and Beryl at this moment returned, magazines under their arms. Mary had a familiar dreamy look on her face as if she had undergone a minor religious experience.

"Mary, it's too bad! First I had to send mother to look up the trains – then Millie and Joan had to go off and get the drinks. You must *help*, Mary. I cannot be expected to do *everything*."

"You try to do too much," Mary said.

"Well – there is so much to do! And what if the train had gone without you?"

Mary made a gesture, as if to indicate that one train is generally followed by another.

"Could you see if they are all right, Mary?"

"I'll go," said Beryl.

"Well..." said Linda, trying to decide what was best: but Beryl had already gone, her long legs threading between the soldiers, several of whom turned to watch her pass. Mary sat down in such a way that she could keep an eye on Beryl's progress. Linda sat facing the other way.

"You must be worried about this week," Mary said.

"Nonsense."

"Well, *I* would be," Mary said simply. "It's been a long time since you've seen Stanley properly, isn't it? You've been so busy, after all."

Linda was mollified by this. "Nearly a year."

"And the children?"

Linda looked over her shoulder towards George, then lowered her voice; not by so much to prevent his hearing her but by enough to make it clear that she didn't want him to. "Longer than that. I doubt if poor George –" here she dropped her voice fractionally lower "– *can even remember his father.*"

"Mother never liked Stanley," Mary said, smoothing a fold in her yellow cotton dress, the dress which Linda always felt was rather eccentric.

"Mary, that's a *terrible* thing to say!" Linda hissed.

Mary shrugged. "Has he taken up with that Mrs Stewart again?" she asked in a normal voice. George at this point stopped listening and began to examine a scab on his knee.

"No," Linda said, not without a certain pride that things were now less bad than previously. "*That* unfortunate episode is over, but..." Her voice trailed off. Mary's manner often had the effect of eliciting half-considered confidences which she often felt she didn't express as well as she might. She sighed, and looked up at the clock.

"Gracious – *where* is mother?"

"She went to check the trains."

"But that was *hours* ago!" If Linda had had her way they would have arrived at Waterloo the previous afternoon.

"Mummy," said Millie breathlessly, "they didn't have orange so we had to get lemonade." She seemed doubtful whether this would be allowed by the complicated rules by which adults organised their conduct. Her life was a constant search for approval and experience had not yet dulled the desire to be cheerful and to do good deeds.

Her mother nodded distractedly, so everything *seemed* alright.

"I wanted orange," George said.

"You said you didn't want *anything*, George," Linda said. George squirmed. "You must say if you want something when you are asked. I am too busy to be guessing." George watched Joan drink her lemonade. Millie sat down next him.

"You can have some of mine," she whispered.

Joan made a 'tsk' noise and sucked loudly on her straw.

"Joan, you're disgusting," said Beryl. Joan pulled a face.

"Mother, where have you been?" Linda said, jumping to her feet. "Mary and I have been *frantic* with worry."

Her mother waited patiently until she had finished talking. "There is a good train in fifteen minutes. Otherwise one waits until three twenty."

"I've never been sure what a 'good' train was," Mary said casually. "Is it a moral judgement?"

"Mary, *what* are you talking about?" said Linda, who hated this kind of frivolity "What mother means, I am sure...what mother *means*, is that we shall not have to *change*."

"Oh, we shall have to change," said her mother.

"Then how is it 'good'?" Mary persisted.

"Is it good because it gets us there sooner?" Millie asked.

Her grandmother smiled. "Yes, my sweet."

"...and we'll see Daddy," Millie went on.

"Yes," Linda said, "we're all going to see Daddy. And go to the seaside," she added, lest the first attraction on its own might prove insufficient.

"And we're all going to have a lovely, lovely time," said their grandmother firmly.

"Is Mr Horse going to be there?" Millie said. "I like Mr Horse, he's funny."

Mr Horse, or Mr McHorslam, was an old business acquaintance of Stanley's and a kind of surrogate grandfather to the children.

"No, I *don't* know if he will be there. Anyway," Linda went on, "if he is there – which he probably won't be – you must be sure to call him 'Mr McHorslam': or perhaps 'Uncle Andrew', seeing as you know him."

"But I call him 'Mr Horse'," Millie said, confused and sad again.

"Mr Horse," George put in, aware that Millie was owed a favour for the lemonade.

"That's enough, children" said Linda. "I had better find another porter. How tiring travelling is." Mary was talking to Beryl and not paying her any attention. "You will discover this, Mary," she said, more loudly, "when you have children. You will discover how very tiring life can be, with responsibilities."

"Linda," Mary said, "tell me what would you like me to do."

"Well...you could see to the children," Linda said. Mary looked round. The children were on their feet, politely waiting for the next move. "And to get a porter would be...ah, poor mother, it's terrible that you should have to simply *slave,*" she said: for her mother had at that moment re-appeared with a porter and was once again supervising the luggage. They moved off in much the same formation as before.

"But I made it clear to the man at the agency that we were to have a compartment to ourselves," Linda said to the steward once they were on the train. "It really is *too* bad..."

"Linda! " Her mother's voice was coming from further down the carriage.

"Mummy!" Millie wailed. The confusion with the reservation had become hopelessly mixed up in her mind with her mother's long-standing fear that they were going to miss the train. George looked away in shame. Constant repetition had not dulled the horror and embarrassment of seeing the female members of his family cry in public.

"Yes!" Linda's voice said, echoing and indistinct, "Mother, what is it now? Goodness, what is the matter?" She came flying down the corridor and into the compartment.

"This is ours," said Mary.

"Well," said Linda, as if there were still something unsatisfactory about it. They all arranged themselves as best they could in the compartment. "Mary, I must face the engine, or I shall get a splitting headache, as you know."

"Is it a steam-engine?" Millie asked again.

"I told you," Joan began, casting up her eyes, "you don't get steam engines on this line, silly." But just then there was a whistle, and the sensation of great pistons grinding together. It *was* a steam engine after all!

Millie danced around her grandmother's feet. She had never felt so vindicated. Little George peered out of the window. Millie gripped his hand with fierce love as the great beast chuffed and wheezed out of the station.

"Millie, please," Linda said, "go and play in the corridor if you must. There is too little space in here for us grown-ups and you children." Beryl stiffened, unsure where her loyalties lay.

Joan looked down at her book, Beryl at her magazine. George was staring open-mouthed at the window. Everything was tearing past so quickly! Outside the window were people and cars and houses and *everything*.

Millie could stand it no more. She rushed out into the corridor, hauled herself up onto the handrail and thrust her head out of the window so her hair streamed. Looking out across the bitter wastes of South London, she felt her heart would burst.

"Oh, what is going to happen now?" she cried.

The engine picked up speed and rhythm, disgorging great grey clouds of steam so that at times it became lost from her view. Two carriages ahead a young man was also leaning out of the window. She waved at him; he smiled and waved back.

"We're going to the seaside!" she shouted, but her words were snatched away on the roar of the roar of the wind.

A hand gripped her shoulder. "What *do* you think you're doing?" her mother shrieked. "Do you want to be killed outright? Go inside this *instant* and sit down. A fine thing that would be for me to have to tell your father!"

Millie returned to the compartment and sat down gingerly next to her brother.

"You cannot imagine, Mary, what it is like, having to watch them *every minute of the day.*"

Linda pursed her lips and examined Mary's features. She felt her sister was smiling at her but with Mary it was hard to tell. Outside, England fluttered past, offering a similarly unfocussed impression of shifting moods. Town, country; hill, dale; field, copse, track and hedgerow – all blurred together like an analogy of passing time. She was unused to such unsettling perceptions. Then the moment passed. Just trees and houses, and motor cars toot-tooting their horns on this bright summer's day and a cricket field speckled with boys in white flannels.

George was a leopard, streaking alongside the train, leaping every obstacle, never tiring, never faltering.

Beryl was also staring out of the window, watching the telegraph poles flick tediously past. She was thinking of her father: how brown his arms and face were, how he smelled of pipe-smoke and warm earth; how Mrs Stewart had hovered in the background, smiling nervously and calling her 'dear'. They had both wanted to please her. It had been the first time she had been aware of adults going out of their way to do this.

George was now in a bright red motor car, roaring across the bright fields, the man at the wheel blasting his horn like a trumpet.

Mary slowly put down her magazine. Her mind was a still lake of reflection. Uncertainties, unhappiness, recriminations for a lost life or hope for a future just beginning – what thoughts disturbed her, what fantasies invaded her cool introspection? Who can tell?

"Mary," Linda began, "I really have the most *splitting* headache. Could you get some tea? And mother has simply *slaved* today, it is too bad. Mary, I am sure mother would like some tea."

Mary stood up. "Of course."

"Can I come?" Millie asked. She was thinking of the man further down the train, waving into the breeze, of the smile on his face. She wanted to wave at him again. She looked round at her family. They didn't smile. Why were they all so sad? She looked at Auntie Mary. She didn't look sad. Millie couldn't think what she looked like.

"Tea with lemon," Linda went on, "if at *all* possible. But that is probably asking too much of this train. And no, Mille, you may *not* go. Leaning out of windows, indeed."

"Tea, tea-with-lemon, tea, orange, orange, orange, tea," Mary said. "Come on, Beryl."

They walked down the corridor, steadying themselves hand-over-hand against the tempestuous motion of the train. Two carriages down, their way was blocked by a young man. He was fashionably hatless.

"Excuse me," Mary said.

He turned and stood back. "The gong, the gong," he said, cupping his hand to his ear.

"I beg your pardon?" Mary said, a light smile in her eyes.

"Lunch. Or is it still 'luncheon' on this line? One must maintain the correct forms, don't you think? It's easy to make a mistake."

"All too easy. It is, in fact, tea-time."

"Ah – tea. Of course. Perhaps you need help?"

Mary indicated Beryl, hitherto a shadow.

The young man graciously indicated temporary defeat. "I see you have the situation *bien en main*. I look forward to seeing you on the way back. Who goes up, on a train, must come down. Or is it whom?"

"Who," Mary said, still with a smile, as she walked past him.

Beryl was breathless. The exchange had been highly charged – but how, exactly? She thought of her father, of the look on his face when he had gently touched Mrs Stewart on the arm in the café in Portsmouth.

Once in the buffet car, Mary took a table and motioned Beryl to sit down. Beryl understood this private snack to be a small rebellion against her mother's tyranny. Nevertheless she said: "mother will be worrying."

"No doubt. Tea for two, please," Mary said to the steward, "and some Madeira cake. We won't be long," she added.

They watched the waiter set the table. Beryl was unused to being served and her instinct was to help. 'Thank you', 'thank you', she murmured as each item, with a delicate curve of the steward's wrist, was placed before them. The steward straightened up and smiled, a slow dreamy smile of vicarious appetite.

Mary lifted the lid of the teapot and swirled the liquid around with a spoon.

Suddenly, the steward was back. "Is there anything wrong with the tea, madam?" he asked.

"Well, it *smells* nice," Mary said dryly, "but we haven't yet poured it, as you can see."

"That's the best part, the pouring," he said, giving Beryl another slow smile.

Mary poured the tea. It gushed proudly from its brown spout, splashing into Beryl's cup. The steward watched the performance carefully, perhaps lest a drop should be spilled and the whole table, as a consequence, have to be relaid. With the carriage bouncing from side to side, and the cup so full, Beryl hardly dared raise it to her lips.

She sat frozen, aware only of the motion of the train ringing through her body and of the faint breathing of the steward close to her ear. A wisp of hair had come down and draped itself across her face like a cobweb. The steward reached forward as the train lurched, his arm brushing her face. His hand was moving across her, and down: down towards the cup which, though gripped in her hand, she saw now was about to be jerked off the table by the movement of the carriage. With a flick of his wrist he straightened it, and was gone.

Mary had watched this with something approaching amusement. After all, what could be safer than a buffet car in the middle of the afternoon?

Beryl took a sip of her tea and broke off a piece of cake. She sat back in her seat and glanced around the buffet car as if taking in for the first time that there were other individual people there, rather than just an amorphous group of strangers.

"Are you looking forward to the holiday?" Mary asked after a moment.

Beryl now seemed younger as she struggled with the uncertainty as to whether the question had been asked of her as a child or as an adult, both being worlds she inhabited. She soon saw that the answer was the same in either case. "No," she said.

"Neither am I," Mary agreed. "I think it could be very difficult. Do you mind, about your father?"

"Well, I did, but...now I'm used to it." Beryl sensed this was not an adequate summary of her complex feelings on the subject. Most difficult to express was her inability to love, still less like, both her parents at the same time; also that she preferred the one she wasn't with. It was as if all their problems of compatibility had transferred themselves to her, leaving them free to live their lives independently of each other.

"And the younger ones?"

This question, Mary at once realised, required an effort of empathy and divination in excess of Beryl's current capacities and was answered with a shrug which might have passed for indifference.

Mary changed the subject and they spoke of trivial things. The waiter reappeared twice, on each occasion giving them little more than a nod. Beryl felt a stirring of pique at this inattention.

They made their way back to their compartment with their order of drinks. The young man was still in the corridor, moodily staring out of the window. His face brightened at their approach.

"How was the tea?"

"Passable," Mary said, "but the Madeira cake was a dry."

"I'm sorry – although dry Madeira cake is hardly the end of the world."

"Indeed not."

"Where do you get off?" he went on casually.

"We change at Bournemouth, for Corfe. That is if the guard is to be believed. The porter told us something quite different."

"Often the only way is to climb along the top of the carriages and ask the driver," the man agreed.

They were at it again, Beryl thought.

"Your tea is getting cold," the man said. "Perhaps we'll meet at Bournemouth? I get off there too."

As they continued down the carriages, Beryl reflected on these exchanges. The sudden squalls which sprung up to disrupt even the simplest-seeming incident were largely unknown to her; rather, she was old enough to recognise them when they happened but too young to see the warning signs of their arrival. Yet with every day, every event, things were becoming clearer. Even such simple events as tea on a train and a chance conversation with a stranger produced lessons and examples as to future conduct.

"Mary, it's too bad," Linda said to them, "I couldn't think *what* had happened to you. Mother and I were *quite* frantic."

Her mother smiled faintly at this and sipped her tea.

"There are so many rough types on a train...soldiers and so forth," Linda Salter continued darkly, as if speaking of wolves.

It was Mary's turn to smile. Beryl watched her aunt's face closely, searching for clues. She found herself smiling as well. This had the effect of throwing Linda into an even worse temper.

"I really don't know what is so funny, either of you."

"There was a queue," Mary said simply.

This was another interesting discovery to Beryl: adults, even members of her family, lied to each other as a matter of course.

"Is a queue when there are lots of people waiting, or is it...is it..?" Millie asked.

"Yes," he mother replied shortly, "and you should remember to let people who have been waiting longer than you go first, Millie. That's *very* important."

Millie flinched at this stinging and unexpected rebuke and tried to peer over Joan's shoulder at her book. Joan kept twisting it away from her before allowing it to slip back so she could do it all over again. Mille sniffed and looked away. It seemed like a boring book anyway. But, ooh – there was a picture of a cat.

"Can we have a cat?" Millie asked.

"A cat?" Linda asked in amazement.

"Cats are stupid," Joan said without looking up.

"Then why are you reading about them?"

"I'm not, so there."

"Yes you are." She grabbed the book out of Joan's hands. There, on the right hand page, was a picture of a cat, but ugly and all thin and pointy. It hardly looked like a cat at all.

"That's an Egyptian cat," Joan said, trying to get the book back.

"Can we have an Egyptian cat?" Millie asked.

"You are giving me a headache," Linda said." There is no question of a cat – the very idea. Do you not think we do not already have enough mouths to feed?"

Millie could not understand this sentence at all.

"George, *don't* play with your drink," Linda said. George was sucking the last drops of orange with his straw.

"If you do that *once* more…"

The whole thing was now much more exciting. George turned towards the window and gave a final defiant suck.

Linda grabbed the glass from George's hand, knocking her mother's elbow so that a few drops of tea spilled onto Mrs Denton's white linen dress.

"There, George. *Look* at what you have done. You grandmother's dress is practically ruined…"

"It's nothing, Linda," her mother said calmly. She would like to have smiled at George, told *him* that it didn't matter but it would have been so *difficult*.

Millie, still thinking of cats, and George, still thinking of his drink, looked at their mother more in disappointment than anger. Beryl, party to a deception of uncertain significance, could not bear to look at her mother at all. Old Mrs Denton did not choose to. Joan continued to look at her book, turning the pages mechanically.

Shortly afterwards they arrived at Basingstoke.

"Goodness," Linda said, "Basingstoke. We change here, I think."

"No," said Mary and her mother at the same time.

"Pardon me, we do." Linda had passed the point where she could accept 'no'. If in doubt, they should change trains, it was as simple as that.

Everyone was forced to their feet, hunting for bags and coats. At that moment a uniformed figure passed the compartment door. Linda shrieked to attract his attention.

"I believe we must change here, for the Purbeck branch." She practically stamped her foot. The man was in no hurry to answer. "Via Bournemouth."

"Do you want to go to Bournemouth?" the man said slowly.

Really, he seemed to be an imbecile, Linda thought.

"Yes, yes," Linda cried, "*first*. We want to go to Bournemouth *first*. But then we have to take the Purbeck branch. To Corfe." She could not see how matters could be made any clearer.

"If you want to go to Bournemouth, you are on the right train," the man said patiently. They started to pull away. Linda retreated into the compartment and threw herself in the seat.

Mary had stepped into the corridor during this exchange. "Thank you," she said to the man.

He smiled. "I don't work for the railway, you know. I'm a postman."

"Yes, I know."

George's bright leopard and fast motor-car had melted into the afternoon. Instead, as the train picked up speed, he was busy hauling the people on the platform into his carriage. They were his soldiers. The last was a man leaning on a piece of machinery near a set of points. George only got him just in time. The man was grateful and gave George a wave as they slid onto the open tracks.

'Basingstoke, Basingstoke,' the signs said as the train pulled away. 'Too late to go *back* , too late to go *back* ,'the wheels reminded Linda. She shut her eyes.

Mrs Denton sighed and smiled sadly at her elder daughter. Why did she *worry* so much? *She* didn't worry. Mary didn't worry. Her husband, dead these ten years, hadn't worried. George, Linda and Mary's brother, killed fifteen years ago in the Normandy landings, hadn't worried. Maybe it would have been better if he had.

"Don't *worry*, mother." Those had been his last words to her, smiling at the doorway of their house in Maidenhead. And two days later he was dead.

Don't worry. None of them did. Except Linda. It was as if she had decided, without reference to the others, that she was going to do all their worrying for them. Linda never had any problem finding things to worry about. The exception was her break from Stanley.

During this she had maintained a strange and unexpected calm, as if the crisis were the still eye in the centre of the never-ending storm of her displeasure.

Mrs Denton pursed her lips as she thought of Stanley. Mary was right in that she did not care for him, but had misjudged the reason. He was too like her George, too handsome and gay and splendidly irresponsible: and his great fault was that he had survived the war whereas her George had not. Mrs Denton did her best to drive this uncharitable thought from her mind. She looked out of the window but there was really nothing to see.

"Linda," Mary said, breaking several minutes of rare peace, "does Stanley know what train we're on?"

"But *course*! I told him that we would be arriving in the late afternoon."

"Yes," Mary said slowly, "but does he know on which train?"

"I can't imagine there will be very many." They were arriving at tea-time: it had been agreed, weeks ago, that they would arrive at tea-time. Matters could not have been made clearer to Stanley

Millie was slowly kicking her heels under her seat. The risk of not being met existed as a vague fear, nowhere near as explicit as that of missing the train in the first place. Despite her mother's calm reaction she felt uneasy; but then she so often did. Family life was a constant procession of traps and battles. She carefully kicked Joan's ankle and felt happier.

And as for Beryl, she felt like an animal waking from a long, deep hibernation. The fear of missing a train caused her no concern. It was more the sense of the thing, the idea that this sort of problem would, from now on, appear more frequently. With a flash of insight, she saw her mother as a disappointed woman and her aunt as a woman still waiting for something to happen to her. Beryl herself felt that way. Then the idea blurred into a view of her family, each locked into their private worlds, so many goods trucks rattling across a flat but subtly changing landscape.

Just then there came a high whistle from the locomotive.

This was too much for George. He swung one knee onto the table under the window, the better to press his nose against the glass. In his excitement he knocked the remainder of his grandmother's tea onto the floor.

There was a roar and a blur of sparks and pistons as another train flashed by in the opposite direction. Their carriage rocked slightly in the swell.

"Goodness," said Mrs Denton.

Millie had her hands over her ears. In the confusion, Joan took the opportunity of kicking her on the shin.

"Woo-woo!" George cried, staring out of the window. Then he was gripped by an even greater wonder. "Look!" He pointed. "The sea."

Millie scrambled to her feet to join him. Even Joan looked up. There it was, a brush-stroke of bluey-grey which almost at once was lost in the bluey-grey horizon.

Joan sniffed. "It's probably an estuary," she said.

The train lurched and shuddered as it crossed sets of points. They were almost there.

"Gracious," Linda said, "we're almost there." Once again, everyone started to get up.

Mary, who found the tensions engendered by her sister's anxieties too much to bear in a confined space, stepped out into the corridor.

"Hello."

She turned round. It was the young man, now hatted and carrying a small suitcase, looking in every way like someone about to get off a train.

"I've just decided to visit Corfe."

"You've 'just decided'?" Mary asked, mock-severe. "We aren't in America," she added, perfectly catching his mood. "People don't ride on trains looking for adventures."

"But they do, absolutely! Think of all the people on this train –" he waved his arm, as if to embrace the universe and every living thing in it. "Some of them have a secret plan to go somewhere and not come back."

They had reached the outskirts of the town. From inside the compartment the sound of Linda's frantic roll-call of possessions was rising as the train slowed.

The man pulled down the window and leaned on the sill, half turning his face towards Mary's. "Don't tell me you've never felt like that." The station was coming into view. "Assuming you *do* come back, when will that be?"

"We're staying for a week," Mary replied, affecting a vague manner.

"A lot may happen in a week."

"It may," Mary said carefully.

"I hear Corfe Castle is pretty. Ramparts and so forth."

"So I believe."

"What's your name, by the way? I almost forgot to ask."

"Mary Denton."

"Maurice Mercier."

"Isn't that French?"

"A long time ago. In fact, one of my ancestors was killed doing something dramatic at Corfe Castle in the time of King John. It's possible I take after him."

"By getting killed?"

"By doing something dramatic."

"Ah."

"I might go there tomorrow. I believe early afternoon is the best time. Around two."

"The problem with family holidays is that things are often planned in advance."

"I've got a sketch pad, a hip flask and a stout stick to beat off the Frenchmen. I can wait."

"Mary…" Linda's voice bristled out of the compartment like an angry dog, "Mary, *please* help with this bag…we're nearly there. George, *do* stop making that noise…"

"Well?"

Mary smiled and turned back to the compartment. "Here, Linda, let me…"

Somehow they managed to get off the train and into the waiting room without losing anything. Linda sat down, mopping her brow. "Our train leaves soon, I think."

"In ten minutes, from that platform there," Mrs Denton said firmly. "One can see the train coming so we need have no fear of missing it."

Millie shuffled up next to George for reassurance but he slid off the bench and mooched sulkily round the room kicking a piece of paper, Stanley Matthews against the world.

"George, please *stop* that." George sat down and started swinging his legs. Linda spoke for some while in a querulous vein about the unreliability of train timetables.

"I'm bored," said George. He had been crossing and uncrossing his legs at an increasingly furious pace.

"Mummy's talking, George," Linda said sharply. Joan sniggered. George bit his lip. He was closer than ever to tears. Why did all his family have to be *girls*? It wasn't fair. "Where would we be if everyone talked at once?"

"The Tower of Babel," Joan said promptly.

"No it wasn't," Millie said, striking blindly at her sister's hateful self-assurance.

"It was. They all went yabber-blabble-yabble-babble to each other and God said 'be quiet' and they wouldn't so he turned them into pillars of salt so they had to shut up."

Linda frowned. Was this actually true?

"Babble-abble-yabble," George suggested. Millie giggled.

"The point is that we should never get anything done," Linda said, realising she had to finish her little sermon for appearances' sake even though all this talk of God and pillars of salt had quite driven the planned message from her mind.

"That's why," Joan went on relentlessly, paying not the slightest heed to this milder conclusion, "it's unlucky to drop salt and if you do you have to throw it over your shoulder or else the devil turns you into statues in hell and you burn and burn forever and ever." Joan addressed this last remark at Millie, who burst into tears.

"Shut up, Joan, you nasty girl," Beryl said with feeling. Mary looked at her approvingly.

At that point their train came wheezing into the station.

"Heavens," said Linda.

The short, final journey from Bournemouth to Corfe passed without incident: that is to say, Linda fretted; the younger children bickered; Beryl stared out of one window; Mrs Denton stared out of the other; and Mary, for the first time in a long while, thought about dramatic events. The outline of the castle rose and fell several times from behind a broken row of hills; then the line dipped into an embankment. Suddenly they were there.

"Corfe, Corfe," the stationmaster called on the platform like a sea-bird.

They piled onto the platform.

"Where's Daddy?"

But Daddy was nowhere to be seen. Linda dispatched Beryl and Mary to scour places where he might be lurking, wreathed in smiles and festooned with inappropriate gifts. They returned with no news.

Linda's earlier optimism had been shattered by his non-arrival. After keeping up appearances for ten minutes, her nerve snapped and she marched off to see the stationmaster. He muttered about 'regulations' but eventually agreed to let her use the telephone. The number rang and rang but no one answered.

She went back to the others. Her family had dispersed to the four corners of the waiting room: Joan with her book on one bench, George making faces at his reflection in the ticket-office glass, Millie mooning around by the doorway to the platform, her mother unpacking one of the bags in search of God-knows-what. Only Mary and Beryl had their eyes fixed on the outside world and all its capricious promises. Mary was staring across the forecourt towards the town and, behind it, the sheep-dappled slopes of the Purbeck Hills; Beryl, at the other window, was considering the curve of the westbound railway lines as they sloped away from the dusty platforms before being lost to view behind a beech copse.

These two were the only fixed points in the room. The others shuffled and scrabbled and flounced somewhere in-between. It seemed to Linda that even the slatted benches were fluttering in the soft evening light, of no more substance than the dusty sunbeams slanting through the window above Mary's head.

"Well," she said, and sat down heavily. No one looked up, no one caught her eye. For the first time that day Linda could not bring herself to complain about anything. There was nothing left to say.

"Well," she said again.

Then she folded her hands in her lap and sat back in the seat, waiting for Stanley to arrive.